THECERAMICSBOOK

EDITED BY EMMANUEL COOPER

Editor: Emmanuel Cooper
Assistant Editor: Fiona Sibley
Design and Production: Ben Eldridge

Assisted by Vivienne Edkins, Joe Mirza and Nerida Thompson

Individual entries in the directory have been supplied by the potters concerned

Front cover image: Joanna Howells; Rear: Sophie Cook; This page: Gabriele Koch;
p5: Karen Downing

The Ceramics Book
First Edition   2006

Previously published as Potters

First Edition	1972	Seventh Edition	1986
Second Edition	1974	Eighth Edition	1989
Third Edition	1975	Ninth Edition	1992
Fourth Edition	1977	Tenth Edition	1994
Fifth Edition	1980	Eleventh Edition	1997
Sixth Edition	1983	Twelfth Edition	2000

ISBN 0-9523576-7-4

Published by Ceramic Review Publishing Ltd,
25 Foubert's Place, London W1F 7QF
© Ceramic Review Publishing Ltd

Contents

Introduction

Of all the crafts practised in this country ceramics is one of the largest, with practitioners ranging from fine artists to potters who produce high-quality tableware. For many people pottery has an innate attraction. The ideas that inform the work, together with the making processes, give the craft a universal appeal.

Welcome to *The Ceramics Book*, which illustrates and gives details of over 280 specially selected potters working today. All are Members and Fellows of the Craft Potters Association (CPA), the national body that promotes the work of leading potters and ceramists. This book serves as a useful guide to the range and diversity of current work, which extends from functional handmade tableware and vessels to sculptural ceramics. *The Ceramics Book* contains photographs of recent work and information on the illustrated potters, together with their contact details. It is an invaluable resource for those wanting to see fine examples of current ceramics and for planning visits to potteries and artists' studios.

I am sure that this new edition will prove as useful a guide to contemporary ceramics as previous editions of *Potters*.

Emmanuel Cooper, Editor

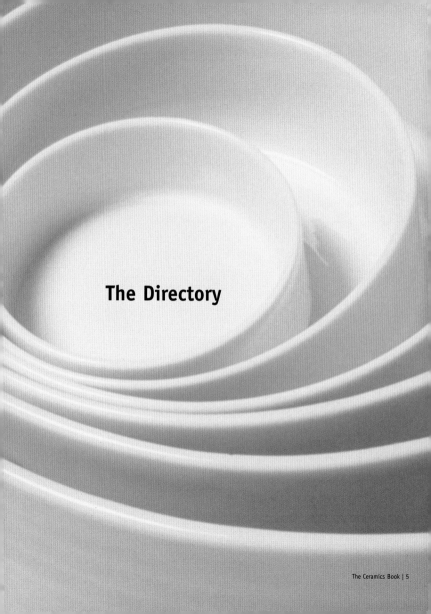

The Directory

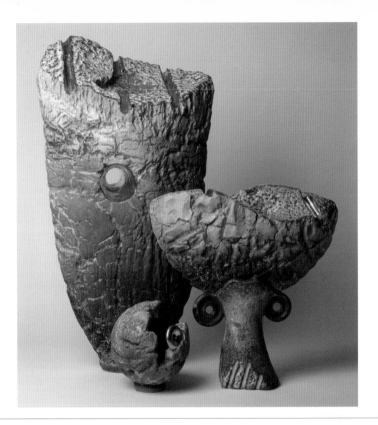

Billy Adams Fellow

My cultural identity, landscape and immediate surroundings strongly influence my work. I consider this association an experiment with form, texture, materials and colour evident within my vessels. I produce this effect by handbuilding a pot, usually from a thrown base, working upwards in several stages. I use three different sorts of clay. First, an interior layer of craft crank. Next, an intermediate layer of clay mixed to prevent shrinkage of the pot during firing. Last, an outer surface of porcelain that is encouraged to buckle and crack as I shape the form from inside the pot. Thus the porcelain retains a fine hard texture, rather than becoming friable. At the midway stage I introduce a stylistically intrusive form such as a regular circular thrown handle or smoothed rim to represent the intervention of humans in the natural world.

4 Allensbank Road, Heath, Cardiff, CF14 3RB Tel 07876 451887
Email adamsfamily@ceramicscardiff.freeserve.co.uk

David Allnatt

I make a range of sculptural ceramics in both earthenware and oxidised stoneware. The forms and textures are inspired by landscapes and the effects of erosion and corrosion found in nature. All of my work is handbuilt using a combination of coiling and press moulding techniques. I have developed my own glazes which produce a dry, matt finish. In combination with metallic oxides I paint, spray and sponge the glazes onto the surface of the work. By using different formulas and firing temperatures I build up the desired surface texture and colour. The pieces are often fired several times before I am satisfied with the results. Examples of my work have been featured in many major exhibitions and have been purchased by both public and private collectors at home and abroad. My workshop can be visited by prior arrangement; I can be contacted by phone and via my website.

Allnatt

3 Poplar Gardens, Napton on the Hill, Warwickshire, CV47 8PG
Tel 01926 813438 Website www.allnattceramics.com

Marilyn Andreetti

I had a traditional training at Farnham (now The Surrey Institute). I taught for some time before starting my own studio. My workshop overlooks a colourful and interesting garden; my work is illustrative and usually depicts flowers, fruit, birds, fishes and occasionally people. Most of it is functional and some of it is commemorative. I use red earthenware clay to make plates, dishes, bowls, jugs and clocks. I decorate with underglaze colours and oxides on a white slip background, and outline with sgraffito. It is bisque-fired and then clear-glazed and fired in an electric kiln to 1100°C. My present work includes garden lanterns made from grogged red clay, fired to 1100°C and decorated with mosaics. It is influenced by Moorish architecture and by the work of Antoni Gaudí. I sell my work in galleries and through craft fairs.

Mud Sweat and Tears Studio Pottery, Belle Vue, 16 Gews Corner, Cheshunt, Hertfordshire, EN8 9BX
Tel 01992 639969 Fax 01992 637258 Email mandreetti@hotmail.co.uk

Tim Andrews Fellow

One-off pieces using raku and smoke techniques. Form and surface are abiding concerns in my work. Incremental and step changes have seen a developing sculptural approach which brings new challenges, both technical and aesthetic. Shapes have evolved along with the use of linear decoration, white and subtly coloured slips which are further muted by the firing process. Recent pieces stem from observations of natural or manmade landscapes such as the rivulet erosion scars of china clay spoil heaps in Cornwall. Utilising the very same materials and harnessing elemental forces to transform them once more is an exciting and rewarding process. Author of *Raku* (A&C Black, UK; Krause, USA, 2005)

Woodbury Studio/Gallery, Greenway, Woodbury, Exeter, EX5 1LW Tel/Fax 01395 233475
Email timandrews@eclipse.co.uk Website www.timandrewsceramics.co.uk
Open Mon-Fri 10am-6pm, Sat 10am-1pm but please ring out of season. Open daily 10am-6pm during exhibitions

Arabella Gail Ark

Ark has distinguished herself in the art
world with her large-scale, architectural
ceramic forms, lending them mystery and
antiquity by firing in the raku tradition.
Previously known as Gail Bakutis.

UK: 38 Cater Gardens, Guildford, Surrey, GU3 3BY Tel 01483 306820
Hawaii: 45-575 Hana Hwy, Hana, Maui, Hawaii 96713 Tel +1 808 248 4890
Email arabella@arkceramics.net Website www.arkceramics.net Visitors welcome to Hawaii studio by appointment

Jacqui Atkin

Jacqui makes burnished, smoke-fired and resist raku-fired forms using various hand-building techniques.

White Cottage, 3 Glyn Morlas, St Martins, Oswestry, SY11 3EE
Tel 01691 773670 Email j.p.atkin@btopenworld.com
Visitors are very welcome but please telephone first – you will need directions.

Felicity Aylieff Fellow

These loosely built vessels, archetypal in form, explore volume, scale and tactility. Pot-bellied and balanced around a central axis they create dramatic silhouettes, with surfaces that add to a sense of movement. Some pieces use dramatic contrasting colour that is saturated with pigment. Others have speckled surfaces, with layers of colour creating an optical interference. As before the works remain sensual and visually intrigu-ing. She exhibits throughout Britain and abroad. She is senior tutor at the Royal College of Art.

F. Aylieff.

Garden Flat, 14 Grosvenor Place, Bath BA1 6AX Tel 01225 334136 (Home) or 01225 313492 (Studio)
Mobile 07714 212124 Email aylieff@btinternet.com or felicity.aylieff@rca.ac.uk

Duncan Ayscough Fellow

I am constantly intrigued by the movement of form and structure when throwing on the potter's wheel: the fluidity of this process combined with firing the pots in sawdust provides a unique form of surface patina. The fine terra sigillata surfaces are broken by darkened areas that follow the form of the pot. I aspire to use these processes as a means of recording the physical and sensual act of making. My works demonstrate my continual concern with oppositional elements; light and dark, night and day, fragile and strong, fluid and rigid. I divide my time between lecturing on the BA and MA Ceramics Programmes at Cardiff School of Art and Design (UWIC) and working from my studio at home in the village of Bethlehem, West Wales.

DA

Farmers, Bethlehem, Carmarthenshire, SA19 9DU   Email duncan@ayscoughceramics.co.uk or dayscough@uwic.ac.uk
Website www.ayscoughceramics.co.uk or www.cardiffceramics.com

Sylph Baier

Trained in Germany and west Wales. Produces
various ranges of domestic ware using slips,
sgraffito and majolica techniques and is currently developing a quiet and sensuous range
in subtle colours.

Chris Barnes

After studying sculpture at art school I was drawn to the functional nature of pots. Pottery still offers a simple solution to the questions about cultural relevance I was asking myself at the time. Form is very important in my pots. I strive for clarity and strength in harmony with the softness of the clay on the wheel. My work is a search for balance and poise. This has taught me to simplify my starting points and clarify my intentions. I am learning to leave space for ambiguity and to be passive enough for the pots to have their own life. Function is still very important to me. Art takes place in use.

The Chocolate Factory, Farleigh Place, Stoke Newington, London, N16 7SX Tel 020 7503 6961 (Studio)
Mobile 07719 454198 Email cb_1959@blueyonder.co.uk Website www.buy-design.co.uk
Visitors welcome by appointment

Richard Baxter

My newest work is wheel thrown in porcelain, which allows me to make pots combining purity of colour, strength and translucency. I particularly like the combination of copper gold pigment and white glaze, which produces a turquoise halo effect. I also make a range of kitchen and tableware in terracotta which can be purchased through my website. I graduated from Loughborough in 1981 and quickly established my first studio with a Crafts Council Setting Up Grant. Since 1991 I have been making and selling pots from my studio and gallery in Old Leigh, Essex, where visitors are always welcome. I sell through other galleries and attend selling fairs.

BAXTER

Old Leigh Studios, 61 High Street, Old Town, Leigh-on-Sea, Essex, SS9 2EP Tel 01702 470490
Email richard@richardbaxter.com Website www.richardbaxter.com Open Tues-Sun 11am-5pm; closed Mon

Deborah Baynes

I am probably better known for my residential summer workshops, which I have held since 1971, originally at White Roding in Essex and since 1993 from Nether Hall. Between courses I have always produced a great many pots. My constant preoccupation has been with throwing and the endless possibilities to be had from manipulating wet clay both on and off the wheel, combined with the alchemy of fire. Since 1986 my work has been almost entirely salt-glazed except for periods spent making raku for the sheer fun of it. In 1997 I had a teaching video made of my throwing techniques. My work is available through various exhibitions and from my workshop. I am a founder member and former chairperson of the East Anglian Potters Association and a member of the Suffolk Craft Society.

Nether Hall, Shotley, Ipswich, Suffolk, IP9 1PW Tel 01473 788300 Fax 01473 787055
Email deb@deborahbaynes.co.uk Website www.potterycourses.net Visitors welcome by appointment

Peter Beard Fellow

Thrown and handbuilt individual pieces mainly in stoneware. The work is vessel and non-vessel based – strong, simple shapes decorated with complex glaze surfaces. Matt and semi-matt glazes are built up in layers which create textural surfaces during the firing, using wax as a resist between layers to create pattern. Heavily textured, monochrome sculptural pieces are also produced using sand-blasting. Exhibited widely in the UK and abroad; work is represented in many public and private collections. Gives lectures and demonstrations in Europe and the UK, and workshop tours of Australia and New Zealand. Awarded various scholarships, most recently a major work development grant from Arts Council England. Author of *Resist and Masking Techniques* (A&C Black). Winner of Inax Design Prize and silver medal, Vallauris Biennale. Member of the International Academy of Ceramics.

PFB

Tanners Cottage, Welsh Road, Cubbington, Leamington Spa, Warwickshire, CV32 7UB
Tel 01926 428481 Email peter@peterbeard.co.uk Website www.peterbeard.co.uk

Beverly Bell-Hughes Fellow

Foundation, Sutton School of Art, 1965-7; Harrow Studio Potters Diploma, under Victor Margrie and Michael Casson, 1967-9. After moving to Wales in 1978 my work developed, relating to the environment where I live, Desanwy Beach and the river estuary of Conwy. I am interested in the tidal system of the sea and the marks left in the sand, driftwood, bones, shells, rocks, erosion. The work is press-moulded and pinched, with other additions of clays and sand. Work is fired to 1300°C in a gas kiln. I do not set out to imitate nature but aspire to echo the process.

Fron Dirion, Conwy Road, Llandudno Junction, Conwy, LL31 9AY Tel 01492 572575
Visitors welcome by appointment

Terry Bell-Hughes Fellow

Trained at Harrow School of Art 1967 under
Victor Margrie and Michael Casson. Primarily
interested in high-fired domestic pots
thrown in series reflecting influences from
Oriental and British country pots. Exhibited
in several solo and many shared exhibitions
in Britain and abroad. Work included in several public and private collections.

Kochevet Bendavid Fellow

I create exotic, luxurious, sensual serving dishes for the special occasions in our lives, the times when we rise above our daily grind, leave behind the mundane and pedestrian and bathe in the glow of beauty, friendship and conviviality. My sumptuous food receptacles are designed to grace and ennoble the dining table, provoke thought and surprise and heighten the shared aesthetic pleasure of the participants. They may provide a topic for talk, a focus for action and attention, and help facilitate interaction between people at the dinner table. I mix a tiny amount of paper fibre with Limoges Porcelain and combine throwing and slab building to make soft, flowing forms. Fluid, lush, coloured glazes are thickly applied. These run into each other, pool in the folds of clay, drip off feet and edges, and so accentuate the sense of overflowing plenty.

147 Overhill Road, East Dulwich, London, SE22 0PT Tel/Fax 020 8516 1241
Email kookiebendavid@hotmail.co.uk Visitors welcome by appointment

Maggie Angus Berkowitz Fellow

I make pictures with glazes on tiles. Work is usually commissioned, often figurative, and always personally designed for a specific site. I enjoy discussing work with clients. Work includes domestic panels for clients in the UK, USA and Japan. Previous work for hospitals, schools, offices, leisure centres, gardens conservatories, Aga-backs and bathrooms have included memorials, games and heraldry. I use oxides, engobes and earthenware glazes on (usually) industrially produced blanks and floor tiles. Trained, taught and worked in the UK, Italy, Tanzania, USA and Japan. Exhibits in the UK and Japan.

21-23 Park Road, Milnthorpe, Cumbria, LA7 7AD Tel/Fax 01539 563970
Email maggie@maggieberkowitz.co.uk Website www.maggieberkowitz.co.uk

John Berry Fellow

Studied architecture at the University of Westminster, painting at Central St Martins and ceramics at Wimbledon School of Art. Since 1986 lives and works in London and France. Work including prints and drawings in the collections of the Tate Gallery, Victoria and Albert Museum, Imperial War Museum, Welsh Arts Council, Bramah Tea and Coffee Museum, KLM (Holland), Museum Sztuki Poland, Hope College and Wooster Art Museums, USA. My pots are handbuilt or press-moulded individual pieces, usually relating to and including the figure, decorated with coloured glazes and lustres on white and buff stoneware.

JOHN BERRY

45 Chancery Lane, Beckenham, Kent, BR3 6NR
Tel 020 8658 0351

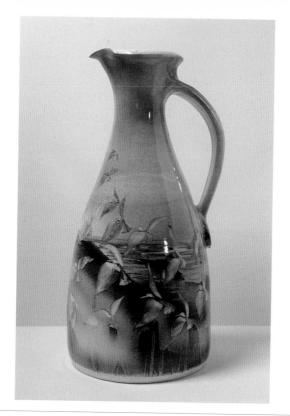

Rob Bibby

I make tin-glazed earthenware fired in an
electric kiln to 1100°C. I decorate by spraying and brushing glaze stains and oxides to
create images of landscape, birds etc. My
work is mainly domestic pottery with some
larger pieces. The workshop is in a converted
chapel, visitors are welcome and can watch
work in progress. I give talks and demonstrations as well as running courses.

Woodnewton Pottery, 43 Main Street, Woodnewton, Oundle, East Northamptonshire, PE8 5EB
Tel 01780 470866 Visitors welcome by appointment

David Binns Fellow

I currently divide my time between my studio in Denbigh, north Wales, and lecturing at the University of Central Lancashire. My work draws inspiration from many disparate sources including forms and textures found in engineering, architecture and the natural landscape. I am interested in challenging and pushing boundaries, continually seeking new material qualities and processes. I am currently exploring kiln casting of ceramic aggregates and glass forming materials, finished through a process of grinding and polishing. I exhibit my work widely throughout the UK and internationally, regularly lecture on my work and have participated in a number of international symposia. Work is featured in numerous books and public and private collections. Member of the International Academy of Ceramics and Crafts Council Index of Selected Makers.

Ty Tal, 34 Park Street, Denbigh, Denbighshire, North Wales, LL16 3DB Tel 01745 814441
Email dsbinns@hotmail.com Website www.davidbinnsceramics.com Visitors welcome by appointment

Matthew Blakely

Softly thrown porcelain pots, often altered,
distorted and indented while wet. Glazed
with fresh aqueous colours that enhance the
softness and movement of the forms and the
purity of the clay.

9 Abbey Lane, Lode, Cambridgeshire, CB5 9EP Tel 01223 811959
Email smashingpots@uk2.net Website www.matthewblakely.co.uk Visitors welcome by appointment

Gill Bliss

Studied ceramics at Cardiff (now UWIC) – BA in 1978 and MA in 1995. Making individual figurative pieces which may be of human or animal subjects. Fragmented forms, such as torsos, heads and hands are used in order to focus on important areas of expression, gesture and character. Each piece is finely modelled using coiling and pinching techniques and a range of clays from terracotta to porcelain paperclay. Finishes include crackle glazes, vitreous slips and smoke firing, with a top temperature of 1260°C. Author of *The Potter's Question and Answer Book* (A&C Black).

Gill Bliss

David Body

I trained at Twickenham College as an illustrator/graphic designer 1963-7 and worked in various advertising agencies and design groups in London before moving to Scotland in 1977. My wife Sally and I set up our first pottery at Scarfskerry, a small village on the north coast of Caithness. We relocated to John O'Groats in 1986 with the subsequent change of name from Scarfskerry Pottery to John O'Groats Pottery. I use various making techniques including throwing, extruding, hand-building and casting to produce individual ceramics and tableware that are either reduction or soda/salt-fired. The Highland landscape is my main source of inspiration. In Caithness the landscape and weather are all-pervasive. Selected elements are used to express the feeling of certain terrain, weather and light conditions. My time is now evenly divided between my pottery and painting.

John O'Groats Pottery, 3 The Craft Centre, John O'Groats, Wick, Caithness KW1 4YR Tel/Fax 01955 611284
Email info@jogpot.co.uk Website www.jogpot.co.uk Open Apr-Sept: daily 9.30am-5.30pm, except Sunday
12.30am-5.30pm; Oct-Mar: Tues-Sat 9.30am-5pm Visitors welcome by appointment

Martin Booth

Since finishing my degree at Loughborough College of Art (1988-91) I have produced work of a sculptural nature. I am inspired in my work by the landscape and by organic growth and erosion. Recent works focus on the journey from the earth to the sky, with forms rooted to the mass of the ground, lifting, twisting and reaching high. My work is made using pipe clay, which is highly textured and fires to a rich terracotta/brown. I use slips and oxides sparingly to enhance form and texture.

MARTIN BOOTH

49 Heaton Terrace, Porthill, Newcastle-under-Lyme, Staffordshire, ST5 8PJ
Tel 01782 639182 Visitors welcome by appointment

Richard Boswell

Hand-thrown earthenware flasks, bottles and bowls. The tactile quality of the work is of great importance to me and this satin white glaze, fired to 1117°C, is very satisfying to handle. Some pieces are very finely decorated with coloured clay inlay.

66 Wallington Shore Road, Fareham, Hampshire, PO16 8SJ
Tel 01329 511497 Email richatwallington@yahoo.co.uk Visitors welcome by appointment

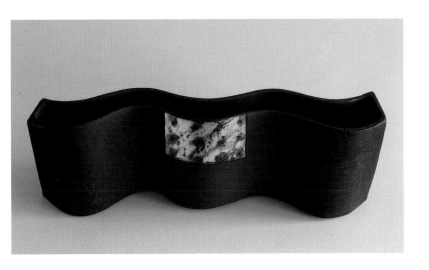

Joy Bosworth Fellow

The work is influenced by an interest in the precision of some of the most mundane objects, altered by time and use and discarded in an urban environment. The vessels are raku-fired and given 'value' by the application of patinated silver leaf, some with silver handles or lids. Educated to MA level at Cardiff and Wolverhampton University, I now teach ceramics to degree level at Birmingham University. I exhibit at potters' markets and in galleries nationally.

22A Worcester Road, Hagley, West Midlands, DY9 0LD
Tel 01562 884810 Email info@joybosworthceramics.com

Clive Bowen Fellow

The pottery was established in 1971. The
pots are thrown in red earthenware clay and
range from large-scale storage jars and garden pots to mugs and egg cups. The domestic ware and one-off pots may be decorated
with contrasting slips using slip trailing,
combing and sgraffito methods. Bowen's pots
are once-fired in a round (8' dia.) downdraught wood-fired kiln to 1040-1060°C
(less for garden pots).

Shebbear Pottery, Shebbear, Beaworthy, Devon, EX21 5QZ Tel 01409 281271
Wholesale and retail customers are welcome at the showroom.

Sheila Boyce

At the ripe old age of forty-eight I decided on a complete career change and studied ceramics and glass at De Montfort University. Since then I have been producing quite large burnished and smoke-fired sculptural forms from my home studio. As with many artists, my imagination is triggered primarily from nature's designs and in particular those found around the beaches of the British Isles. My inspiration comes not only from the wealth of spontaneous designs, textures and forms, but from the invigorating feeling that I get wandering the beaches in virtual isolation on cold and windy days in winter and spring. I show my work regularly at selected galleries and events nationally and have provided work for collections in America and Switzerland, as well as commission pieces for the *Arcadia* Cruise Ship.

36 Gwendolin Avenue, Birstall, Leicester, LE4 4HD Tel 0116 220 7105
Email oncefired@aol.com Website www.oncefired.co.uk Visitors welcome by appointment

Loretta Braganza Fellow

Trained in graphics with a fine arts background. Makes handbuilt sculptural forms. Strong abstract shapes are linked by deceptively simple surface patterning. The linear decorative technique is constantly evolving using coloured slip and underglaze colours. Work in public, corporate and private collections in Britain and abroad.

Braganza
LMB

The Coach House, 198 Mount Vale, York, YO24 1DL Tel 01904 630454
Email loretta@braganzas.freeserve.co.uk Visitors welcome by appointment

Benedict Brierley

My work is concerned with the malleability of material through making and firing. I endeavour to capture the softness of wheel-thrown clay in the finished objects. My work revolves around a concept of function, sometimes breaking through into it and sometimes referencing it. Forms are informed by early animated film such as *The Sorcerer's Apprentice* where domestic utilitarian objects are anthropomorphised, taking on human gestures. All pieces are fired in wood-fired anagama kilns for three to five days using the pyroplasticity, fly ash and flame flashing of the firing to accentuate the softness of form. I have developed several clays and porcelains which respond directly to the atmosphere and duration of a wood firing. Some of this work is partially glazed with titanium ash glaze, nuka and carbon trapping shinos. All pieces are assembled and altered while soft on the wheel.

Benedict Brierley

25 Turner Avenue, Loughborough, Leicestershire, LE11 2DA
Tel 01509 828349 Email benedict@supanet.com Visitors welcome by appointment

David Brown

After thirty years largely devoted to teaching others, David Brown retired in 1999 to concentrate more fully on producing his own work. He has long been recognised for his expertise in designing and making teapots in a variety of styles, and more recently for his turquoise and mauve ranges of glazes and textural surfaces applied to a range of vessels. This work often reflects his long term interest in sea and sky as well as rocks, minerals and fossils. David works mainly in a smooth, pale stoneware clay, firing in an electric kiln to a temperature of 1250°C. David is a member of Westcountry Potters Association and Somerset Guild of Craftsmen.
(Photo: Justin Orwin)

DB Pottery, Church Street, Merriott, Somerset, TA16 5PR Tel 01460 75655
Showroom open most days but advisable to phone first

Melanie Brown

I throw and turn my work in porcelain. I respond to its purity, and the glazes that I use – chun, *sang de boeuf* and flambé – are crisp and vibrant against the whiteness of the body. I make teapots, as I am fascinated by the three-dimensional jigsaw puzzle that is necessary to get the elements to work together to form the whole. The handles are custom-made for each piece using cane and silver. I believe it is important that the

integrity of function and craftsmanship should be complemented by aesthetic considerations; the ergonomics of each piece is part of its beauty. Recently I have started to make 'families' – sets of eight or ten pieces which have all been thrown, turned, glazed and – most importantly – fired together. These are then shown together so that the variations of colour caused by atmospheric changes within the kiln are visible on the work.

M

Garden Cottage, Coldbrook, Abergavenny, Monmouthshire, NP7 9ST
Tel 01873 858015 Email mel@artwks.co.uk Visitors welcome by appointment

Sandy Brown Fellow

Trained in Daisei Pottery, Mashiko, Japan. Widely exhibited worldwide with work in numerous public collections in the UK, including the Victoria and Albert Museum and many abroad. Currently working on a major Arts Council funded project, *Ritual: The Still Point and The Dance*. *The Still Point* is a contemporary tea ceremony as meditation, and *The Dance* is an installation of architectural scale sculptural work express-

ing the energy which comes from *The Still Point*. Does Spontaneity Performance for festivals. Runs occasional courses, *Creativity is Play*, on developing one's creativity.

3 Marine Parade, Appledore, Bideford, Devon, EX39 1PJ Tel 01237 478219
Email sandy@sandybrown.freeserve.co.uk Website www.sandybrownarts.com
Visitors welcome by appointment to studio and exhibition space in Glove Factory

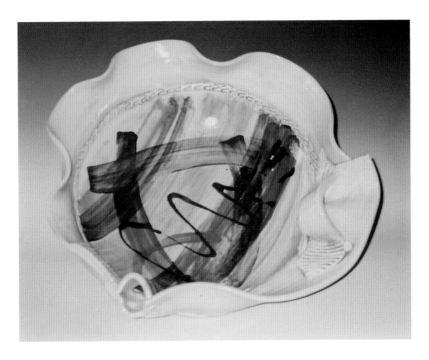

Susan Bruce

I trained at Cheltenham and Lowestoft colleges of art and have been a potter as well as a part-time art teacher since then. I have exhibited my work widely. My range of functional white earthenware has a painterly approach to decoration using simple brush strokes of coloured slips with a transparent glaze. The work is thrown and altered, and the bases and spouts are handbuilt from textured clay. I also make one-off dishes with thrown and altered rims. These are influenced by the changing scenery of the river estuary close to where I live, marks made on the mud at low tide, the reeds near the shore and the variety of bird life. I am the author of the book, *The Art of Handbuilt Ceramics*, and a member of the Suffolk Craft Society.

4 Pinewood, Woodbridge, Suffolk, IP12 4DS Tel 01394 384865
Email susanbruce@ceramics33.freeserve.co.uk

Victoria Bryan

Victoria Bryan makes porcelain domestic ware which is decorated with ceramic pencils, slips and stains.

Fig Tree House, 19 Northdown Avenue, Cliftonville, Margate, Kent, CT9 2NL
Mobile 07973 898473   Fax 01843 297919   No showroom; visitors welcome by appointment

Karen Bunting

Elegant domestic ceramics, including jugs, vases, bowls and tea bowls, in reduced stoneware. Each piece is initially thrown, then individually worked and decorated. Stripes, spots and crosshatching help map out surfaces and reveal aspects of form. The colours are subdued blues, smoky greys and deep blacks. The resulting pots are unique but share a family resemblance. The work is characterised by a cohesion between form and decoration and has a peaceful, self-possessed quality.

53 Beck Road, London, E8 4RE Tel 020 7249 3016
Email bunting.all@virgin.net Visitors welcome by appointment

Jan Bunyan

Contemporary ceramic tableware. I make
slipped and brush-decorated earthenware,
trying to achieve clarity of form and fresh,
lively decoration. My pots are for use and
are mainly thrown but with some handbuilding.

4 Bridge Road, Butlers Marston, Warwick, CV35 0ND Tel 01926 641560
Email janbunyan@butlersmarston.fsnet.co.uk Visitors welcome by appointment

The Ceramics Book | 42

Deirdre Burnett Fellow

Studied sculpture at St Martins School of Art and then took a BA in ceramics at Camberwell School of Art. Makes individual vessel forms in oxidised stoneware and porcelain. Mostly wheel-thrown, turned and altered, although large floor-standing pieces are handbuilt. Volcanic, reactive or colour surface qualities come from oxides and materials thrown or laminated in the body. Alternatively from slips and glazes which react to each other, not simply glazes applied to the surface. All the glaze effects are controlled accidents, chemical reactions held fossilised by heat control. Work in many private and public collections including Museum of Modem Art, New York; Victoria and Albert Museum, London; Museum Boymans-van Beuningen, Rotterdam; National Gallery of Victoria, Melbourne, Australia; Sainsbury Collection, Norwich. On the Crafts Council Index of Selected Makers.

48 Gipsy Hill, London, SE19 1NL Tel 020 8670 6565
Email deirdreburnett@btinternet.com Visitors welcome by appointment

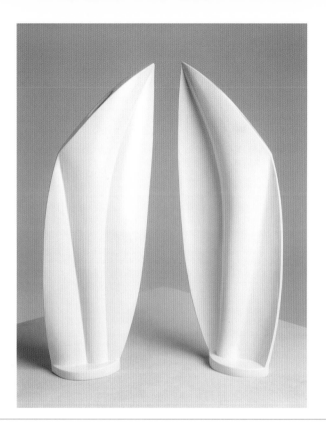

Ian Byers Fellow

The image of the horse, initially stylised, more recently moving towards an almost abstract sensibility, has been the focal point of work during the past ten years. From this source have sprung both large outdoor sculptures and more intimate pieces. The work is sometimes handbuilt, at other times employing intermediate stages of model making before the work is press-moulded or cast. Ian Byers teaches at Bath Spa University College on the BA Ceramics course and has taught, lectured and exhibited in England and Europe.

16 Stroud Road, London, SE25 5DR
Tel 020 8654 0225 Email ianbyersceramics@hotmail.com

John Calver Fellow

John Calver makes functional stoneware at
his studio in North Lancashire. Simple or
dynamically altered forms are finished with
high fire reduction glazes. Over the past fifteen years John has given regular workshops
and demonstrations in the UK, Australia,
New Zealand, Canada and the USA.

23 Silverdale Road, Yealand Redmayne, Carnforth, Lancashire, LA5 9TA
Tel 01524 781362 Email calver@freenet.co.uk
Visitors are welcome at the workshop but unusual working hours makes telephoning first advisable

Kyra Cane Fellow

The pots that I make explore simple formats, working in series to gradually extend the boundaries of the ceramic structures that are my current obsession; making subtle changes until the pieces develop a voice which has a resonance that interests and excites me. Pieces are thrown on a wheel, an intense, physical process that demands immediate responses to material and form; surfaces react to the slightest touch, traces of hand and tools remain, the indents and hollows created by fingers and fists interrupt and contradict symmetry. Bold, ostensibly black marks wrap themselves around the porcelain forms, describing and defining spaces; brushmarks fade and blur, inky opaque bands change to pale fresh air blues. There are remnants in these vessels of the vast landscapes which have always been my inspiration.

5 West Workshops, Harley Foundation, Welbeck, Worksop, Nottinghamshire, S80 3LW
Tel 01909 489555 Email kc-jb@ntlworld.com

Daphne Carnegy Fellow

Daphne Carnegy studied pottery as an apprentice to a faience potter in France and subsequently at the Harrow Studio Pottery course. Since 1980 she has had her own workshop in London, producing thrown and painted tin-glazed earthenware in the maiolica tradition. She aims to combine the highly decorative, exhilarating qualities of maiolica with functional pottery for every-day use – the forms, colours and patterns all intended to enhance enjoyment of food and drink. Fruit and floral designs are expressed in a bold Mediterranean palette but more recent abstract designs explore subtler tones. Daphne is the author of *Tin-glazed Earthenware* (A&C Black, 1993).

Kingsgate Workshops, 110–116 Kingsgate Road, London, NW6 2JG Tel 020 7328 2051 or 020 8442 0337
Email d.carnegy@tiscali.co.uk Visitors welcome by appointment

The Ceramics Book | 47

Simon Carroll

His work makes reference to the long English earthenware tradition, to function and to use of the vessel as part of the domestic scene. With deceptive skill, he produces objects that play about with these aspects to create objects that relate to the times in which we live. They are partly disconcerting, partly reassuring but always witty and accessible. They merge art and craft into a seamless whole. (Emmanuel Cooper)

Unit 4C, The Airfield, St Merryn, Padstow, Cornwall, PL28 8PU
Tel 01841 520072 Website www.simoncarroll.co.uk Visitors welcome by appointment

The Ceramics Book | 48

Sheila Casson Honorary Fellow

Early member of the CPA, 1958. I make
thrown, salt-glazed, stoneware domestic pots,
fired in a gas reduction kiln to 1300°C. I also
make handbuilt vessel forms in red clay which
are burnished and then fired to 1000°C, followed by a smoke firing in a sawdust kiln. I
find the handbuilding very satisfying because
the slower method allows me to concentrate
on the form. The inspiration for all my pots
comes from early Mediterranean wares.

Wobage Farm, Upton Bishop, Ross-on-Wye, Herefordshire, HR9 7QP Tel 01989 780233
Fax 01989 780495 Wobage Makers Gallery open Apr-Sept: Thurs-Sun 10am-5pm;
Oct-Mar: Sat-Sun only; other times by appointment only

Trevor Chaplin

For the past ten years I have made soda vapour-glazed pottery, mainly wheel-based, and altered with some handbuilding. It started in the 1950s whilst holidaying in Cornwall. We visited the many small potteries as tourists, and the seed was sown. In the 1960s I trained in architecture, but later gave this up to study ceramics during 1970-3 then taught for seventeen years. By that time I had established my studio in Wiltshire

and it was only a matter of time before I began potting full-time. I was then making reduction stoneware using shino and ash glazes. Now, all my work is soda-glazed using thick slips to decorate and texture my pots. My present kiln is gas-fired, but I plan to build a wood-fired kiln in the near future.

Marridge Hill Cottage, Ramsbury, Marlborough, Wiltshire, SN8 2HG
Tel 01672 520486 Visitors welcome by appointment

Linda Chew Fellow

After graduating from Cheltenham College of Art in 1973 with a degree in sculpture, I worked for Beth Blik before gaining my Art Teacher's Certificate from London University and set up my workshop in 1975 while teaching in Winchester. My ideas are influenced by a love of textiles, the movement within their patterns, plus a desire to produce pieces that appear soft and tactile. Shaped slabs of porcelain and T material are impressed with lace, haberdashery, netting etc. and assembled. After a biscuit firing, patterns created are then embellished with oxides and underglaze colours over wax resist, and fired to 1260°C in an electric kiln.

42 Cheriton Road, Winchester, Hampshire, SO22 5AY Tel 01962 867218 Email chewceramics@yahoo.com
Work can be viewed at www.ruffordceramiccentre.org.uk www.southernceramicgroup.co.uk www.bluestonegallery.com
Visitors welcome by appointment

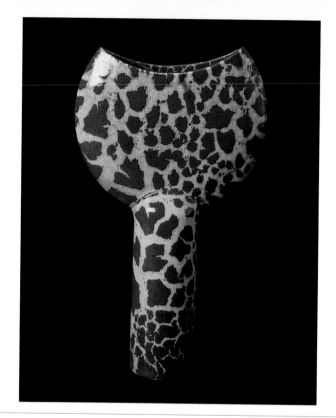

Bruce Chivers

Born and trained in Australia. Moved to
Devon in 1985. He produces individual
thrown pots in porcelain, utilising both
high-fired and raku techniques. He regularly
lectures and demonstrates and his work is
represented in public and private collections. He exhibits throughout the UK,
Europe and the USA.

The School House, Dunsford, Exeter, Devon, EX6 7DD Tel 01647 252099
Email brucechivers@talk21.com Website www.brucechivers.co.uk Visitors welcome by appointment

Kevin de Choisy Fellow

Born in 1954. Attended Harrow School of Art
in the mid 1970s then from 1978-80 he spent
time in New Mexico and Arizona studying
Pueblo Indian Pottery. He returned to
America in 1984 to work as a thrower and
designer for the Rowe Pottery Works in
Wisconsin making blue and grey saltglaze.
Kevin now lives in Somerset and makes a
range of functional pots inspired by Whieldon
and eighteenth-century cream wares.

50 Bove Town, Glastonbury, Somerset, BA6 8JE Tel 01458 835055
Email glazedandconfused@tiscali.co.uk Visitors welcome by appointment

Peter Clough Fellow

I have been making ceramics now for over forty years, and having retired from lecturing am now working full-time. I currently work in porcelain using both throwing and handbuilding processes. Decoration references the landscape here in Yorkshire. My work has been exhibited widely in the UK and in Germany, Switzerland and New Zealand and is held in many private and public collections. I am a former Chair of the Northern Potters Association and current council member of the Craft Potters Association.

8 Southville Terrace, Harrogate, North Yorkshire, HG1 3HH   Tel 01423 567716   Mobile 07787 521089
Email potclough@hotmail.com   Website www.peterclough.com   Visitors welcome by appointment

Russell Coates Fellow

I make underglaze blue enamelled porcelain in the style of Kutani ware which I studied in Japan. I start the decoration with a tissue paper and charcoal pattern transfer system to get the geometric design onto the biscuited pot and complete the fish, animals and birds freehand in pencil. These are painted in underglaze blue, glazed and fired to 1270°C. The design is completed with enamels and sometimes gold, then fired for a third time to 840°C. I have various sea creature designs with dolphins, a coral reef and Northern waters; a variety of bird and deer in forest designs and a North African theme inspired by a commission of ceramic wall pieces for the Medina Restaurant of the P&O liner *Aurora*. Recently the Spode factory have reproduced some of my designs as limited editions and derivative works backstamped *Russell Coates by Spode* as part of their *Natural World* series.

The Haven, Gare Hill Road, Witham Friary, Frome, Somerset, BA11 5EX
Tel 01373 836171 Mobile 07745 477135 Visitors welcome by appointment

Roger Cockram Fellow

Studied ceramics at Harrow in the 1970s. Early work was wood-fired stoneware (ten years). Work since is derived from observations and drawings from the natural world of water: its movements and rhythms, colours and textures are major preoccupations. The influence of water on the terrain around it and the life found in it also figure strongly. Also makes a small range of pots for use. All work is once-fired to cone 10/11 in reduc-tion. Sells through own showroom, galleries and fairs in UK and elsewhere; also exhibitions, commissions and the internet.

Chittlehampton Pottery and Gallery, Chittlehampton, North Devon, EX37 9PX Tel 01769 540420
Email roger@rogercockram-ceramics.co.uk Website www.rogercockram-ceramics.co.uk
Open Mon–Fri 10am–1pm, 2–5.30pm; also often open at weekends or by request; telephone first

Elaine Coles

I spent 1972-4 in Botswana, southern Africa where I became fascinated by ethnic designs, which have been a great influence in my work. My current work is thrown, the decoration inspired by Howard Hodgkin. I use the surface of the pot as a canvas, mark-making with brushes and trailers. They are then fired in a gas kiln to 1280°C. The firing is crucial and at high temperature the glazes melt and run into each other, creating abstract designs individual to each piece, intended either to be used or as a decorative piece of art. I also make handbuilt vessels using slabs and coils. Dry glazes or raku firings enhance the inlaid, pieced and patched surface of the vessel, signifying an ancient quality and 'feel'. Originally self-taught, in 1987 I did the Diploma course at Goldsmiths College. My workshop is at the Bank Gallery in Chobham.

Elaine Coles

Chobham Pottery, 73A High Street, Chobham, Surrey, GU24 8AF Tel 01276 856769
Email pottery@ecoles.go-plus.net Website www.elainecoles.co.uk Visitors welcome by appointment

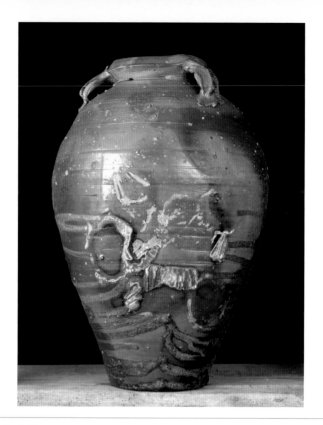

Nic Collins Fellow

My work is made using clay local to the
area, mainly the Meeth quarry in North
Devon. I fire using wood as a fuel in an
anagama kiln. My pots rely on ash and flame
markings from the four-day firing to achieve
a buildup of texture and colour. The pots are
signed.

The Barn Pottery, North Bovey Road, Moretonhampstead, Devon, TQ13 8PQ Tel 01647 441198
Email nic.collins4@btopenworld.com Visitors welcome by appointment

Jennifer Colquitt

My studio has been based in Dudley town centre for several years. I use fine quality porcelain to produce textured and intricate wall panels. These panels are coloured with oxides and metallic lustres during a course of three firings. The main themes used are trees, leaves and flowers combined with the playful and direct qualities of naïve art. I am very interested in traditional patterns, often incorporating these into borders and edges. Porcelain fascinates me as a material as it combines fragility with great strength. To realise its true qualities it has to withstand very high temperatures. This is always a challenge.

Jennifer Colquitt 05

Field Ceramics, Holloway Chambers, 27 Priory Street, Dudley, West Midlands, DY1 1HA
Tel 01384 455591 Visitors welcome by appointment

The Ceramics Book | 59

Jo Connell

I work experimentally with coloured clays which I layer, marble and stretch, making sculptural vessels and wall panels, sometimes combining mixed media. The clay surface is often highly textured and generally unglazed. My inspiration comes from the natural world – land and seascape, rock strata, plant growth, patterns made by water – and from an enjoyment of the working properties of clay itself. Initially trained at North Staffordshire Polytechnic (1972), taught for many years in schools and colleges. Author of *The Potter's Guide to Ceramic Surfaces* (Apple Press).

Witherley Lodge, 12 Watling Street, Witherley, Atherstone, Warwickshire, CV9 1RD Tel 01827 712128
Email jo@jjconnell.co.uk Website www.jjconnell.co.uk Visitors welcome by appointment

Clare Conrad

Individual stoneware pots distinctive for
their painterly exploration of colour and
texture, inspired mainly by the effects of
light and ageing on architecture. Her technique of layering vitreous slip onto finely-
thrown vessels and vases provides a rugged
texture which contrasts with the satin-matt
glaze inside. Has exhibited widely throughout the UK, America and Japan and has
work in private and public collections.

29 Westcourt Lane, Shepherdswell, Nr Dover, Kent, CT15 7PT
Tel/Fax 01304 831019 Email clareconrad@hotmail.com

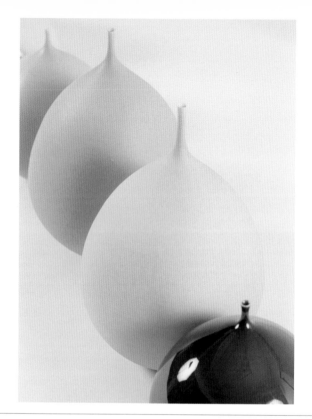

Sophie Cook

Studied at Camberwell College of Art, graduating in 1997. Specialising in thrown porcelain pod and bottle forms. Work is sold worldwide, stockists can be found on the website. Permanent collections include the Geffrye Museum, London and collectors range from Elton John to Giorgio Armani.

Cockpit Arts, Studio 109, 18-22 Creekside, Deptford, London, SE8 3DZ Tel 020 8694 8363
Website www.sophiecook.com Visitors welcome by appointment. Seconds sale twice a year

Delan Cookson Fellow

My present work comprises a range of thrown porcelain bottles, bowls and vases. Each pot is an individual variation of a classic form. I use porcelain because of its delicacy and whiteness. Typically these pots are covered by a silky blue transluscent glaze of variable intensity. This colour and the purity of form evoke calmness, and these pots work well as decorative elements in modern interiors. My workshop overlooks Hayle estuary in Cornwall which is a constant inspiration.

3 King George Memorial Walk, Phillack, Hayle, Cornwall, TR27 5AA Tel 01736 755254
Email delancookson@hotmail.com Visitors welcome by appointment

Emmanuel Cooper Fellow

Individual pots, mostly in porcelain, including bowls and jug forms. Glazes tend to be bright and rich and include turquoise blues and greens, nickel pinks and yolk yellows. All are fired to 1260°C in an electric kiln. Has been making pots since 1965. Editor of *Ceramic Review*. Major recent exhibitions at Fine Art Society, London; Crafts Study Centre, Farnham; Peter Scott Gallery, Lancaster. Work in Victoria and Albert Museum, Royal Scottish Museum, Crafts Council Collection. Author of *Ten Thousand Years of Pottery* (British Museum Press) and *Bernard Leach: Life and Work* (Yale University Press).

Fonthill Pottery, 38 Chalcot Road, London, NW1 8LP Tel 020 7722 9090 Mobile 07973 816407
Email emmanuelcooper@lineone.net Visitors welcome by appointment

Prue Cooper

Prue Cooper trained as a painter in the 1960s and spent twenty years dealing in drawings before deciding to go back to making things. After a three-year ceramic course she set up her own studio with Regina Heinz in 1996. Her dishes are meant to be used, and celebrate friendship, generosity and the sharing of simple pleasures. The simple press-moulded shapes are sometimes decorated with inscriptions, the overall design of the dish echoing the sense of the words. The dishes are earthenware decorated with slip which is trailed, brushed, printed or sgraffittoed, and glazed with a food-safe glaze. They are dishwater proof and gently oven-proof.

Studio 213E, Wandsworth Business Village, Broomhill Road, London, SW18 4JQ Tel 020 8871 5118
Email info@pruecooper.co.uk Website www.pruecooper.co.uk Visitors welcome by appointment

Gilles Le Corre Fellow

Trained at Camberwell School of Arts and Crafts. My work is made of thrown functional stoneware, fired in a reduction atmosphere, with glazes that are dipped, brushed and trailed. My pots evolve from previous forms, carrying through ideas from one to another, freely manipulating or incising individual pieces in the soft clay. My fascination and development with high-fire glaze decoration leads me to simplify shapes, allowing surface texture to express qualities found in landscapes, stones and archaeological artefacts. (Photo: Chris Honeywell)

19 Howard Street, Oxford, OX4 3AY Tel 01865 245289
Email elaine@lecorre5.wanadoo.co.uk Visitors welcome by appointment

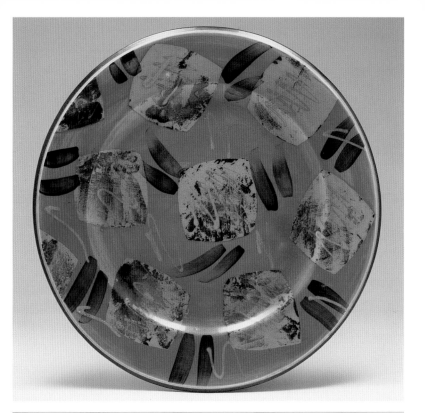

Jane Cox

Trained at Camberwell School of Art (1989-92) and the Royal College of Art (1992-4) and now pots from her studio in Brockley, south London. Makes earthenware tableware using various techniques (throwing, casting, jolleying and handbuilding) and combines bold elegant forms with energetic, striking surface patterns. Uses a method of slip decoration whereby layers are elaborately built up upon one another and then enhanced through the use of coloured transparent glazes. Whilst making items that can be used every day, her main interest is in making vessels that will transcend this, bringing beauty and meaning to our daily lives. (Photo: Nigel Swift)

85 Wickham Road, Brockley, London, SE4 1NH Tel/Fax 020 8692 6742
Email jane@janecoxceramics.com Website www.janecoxceramics.com Visitors welcome by appointment

Sylvia Dales

I trained at Harrow School of Art (1970-2)
and make functional pots for everyday use. I
am influenced by classical forms from different cultures. Pots are mostly thrown and
sometimes altered for oval forms. I work
with French stoneware clay and exclusively
with shino, ash and celadon glazes as I love
the colours these glazes give me. The pots
are then fired to 1300°C in a reduction
glaze.

Sylvia Dales

75/77 Melford Road, Sudbury, Suffolk, CO10 1JT Tel 01787 374581 or 01787 378434
Email pots@sylviedales.fslife.co.uk Visitors welcome

Louise Darby

Louise Darby has gained a reputation for finely thrown stoneware and porcelain. She has made the technique of incising and carving designs into the leatherhard clay very much her own. In pleasing contrast to these animated pieces there are those where she uses simple wax resist banding. A professional potter since graduating from Loughborough in 1978, she works from her rural studio home near Stratford-upon-Avon.

She sells through some fifteen galleries in Britain and overseas, and from her studio.

Clay Barn, Redhill, Alcester, Warwickshire, B49 6NQ
Tel 01789 765214 Email louise.darby@btopenworld.com

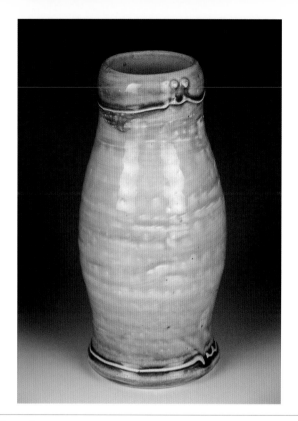

Patia Davis

Studied pottery at Harrow (1986-8) and
Cardiff (1988-90) before coming to
Herefordshire in 1991 to join Wobage Farm
Craft Workshops. Using a Saviac kickwheel I
work with stoneware and porcelain clays to
produce a range of domestic ware. The colours
are achieved by using a combination of iron
rich slips, under a feldspathic glaze, and fired
in a gas kiln to 1300°C. I am currently experimenting making earthenware tiles.

Wobage Farm, Upton Bishop, Ross-on-Wye, Herefordshire, HR9 7QP Tel/Fax 01989 780495
Wobage Makers Gallery open Apr-Sept: Thurs-Sun 10am-5pm;
Oct-Mar: Sat-Sun only; other times by appointment only

Joyce Davison

After many years of teaching, changed to
pottery and has worked in Castle Acre,
Norfolk for about eighteen years. Makes one-
off pieces – jugs, bowls, bottles and platters
in stoneware and porcelain, with decoration
using wax resist, brushwork and fluting.

Ranters, 75 Pales Green, Castle Acre, Norfolk, PE32 2AL Tel 01760 755405
Email joycedavison.ranters@virgin.net Visitors welcome by appointment

The Ceramics Book | 71

John Dawson

Trained initially as a musician at Trinity College of Music, London, studying the organ and harpsichord and was drawn to the music of the Baroque period. Later attended the very last ceramics course at Goldsmiths College (1992-3) specialising in thrown porcelain. I make functional but decorative pieces using either a black satin matt glaze or a simple celadon crackle glaze. My work has strong parallels with my music; a simple form is embellished or decorated to enhance the simplicity and the sense of movement within the form.

47 Heathwood Gardens, Charlton, London, SE7 8ES Tel 020 8316 1919 Email john16749@btinternet.com
Website www.btinternet.com/~john16749 Visitors welcome by appointment

Richard Dewar Fellow

Nothing's changed folks, they're all still
pots.

Dewar

Keryavec, 56550 Locoal-Mendon, France
Email dewar.ceramics@wanadoo.fr Website perso.wanadoo.fr/dewar.ceramics

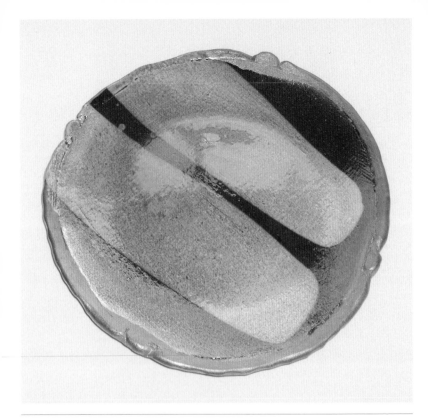

Peter and Jill Dick Fellows

Coxwold Pottery is a small country workshop established in 1965 by Peter and Jill Dick. Together they make a wide variety of work for kitchen, table and garden. Around half the production is earthenware, thrown and decorated with lively coloured slips, but these days more pots are fired to stoneware in the reducing gas kiln, which gives quieter more subtle glaze quality. Jill is well known for her range of green/cream serving dishes while Peter, who trained with Michael Cardew and Ray Finch, greatly enjoys making larger platters and more unusual pieces often with modelled animal motifs. The village of Coxwold lies in pleasant countryside some twenty miles North of York. The showroom and pottery garden are open to the public, but it is essential to phone in advance of a visit.

Coxwold Pottery, Coxwold, York, YO61 4AA Tel 01347 868344 Email info@coxwoldpottery.co.uk
Website www.coxwoldpottery.co.uk Visitors welcome to the showroom and pottery garden by appointment

The Ceramics Book | 74

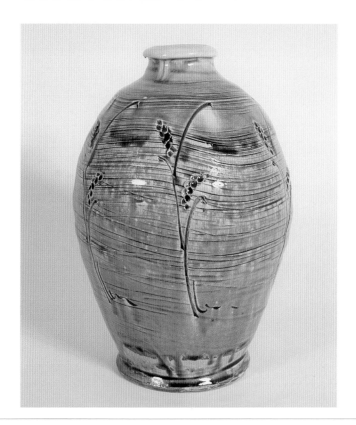

Mike Dodd Fellow

'I love the process of discovery, of letting go, of allowing one's aliveness its own unique play – it's fascinating to watch and to be absorbed by this relationship between disciplined technique and the free play of the heart.' (From Mike Dodd, *An Autobiography of Sorts*.) Reduction glazes, oil-fired – mostly unrefined natural glaze materials e.g. granites, hornfels, basalt, ochre, various wood ashes and local clays.

The Pottery, Dove Workshops, Barton Road, Butleigh, Glastonbury, Somerset, BA6 8TL Tel/Fax 01458 850385
Email mdodd@clara.co.uk Website www.mikedodd.info Visitors welcome by appointment

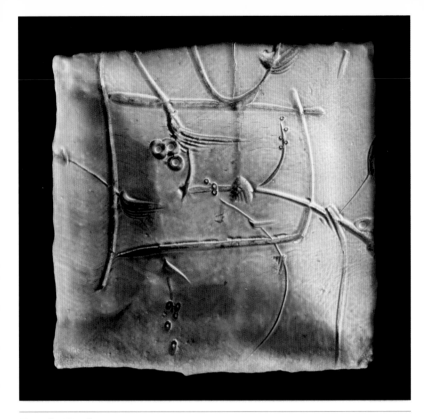

Jack Doherty Fellow

Porcelain, thrown and slab-built with
coloured clays. All the work is soda-fired.
His work can be seen in the collections of
the following museums: Ulster, Stoke-on-
Trent, Liverpool, Cheltenham,
Keramiekmuseum het Princesshof,
Leewarden, Holland. Currently chair of the
Craft Potters Association (2006).

Hooks Cottage, Lea Bailey, Ross-on-Wye, Herefordshire, HR9 5TY Tel/Fax 01989 750644
Email jack.doherty@virgin.net Website www.dohertyporcelain.com
Visitors welcome at the workshop and showroom by appointment

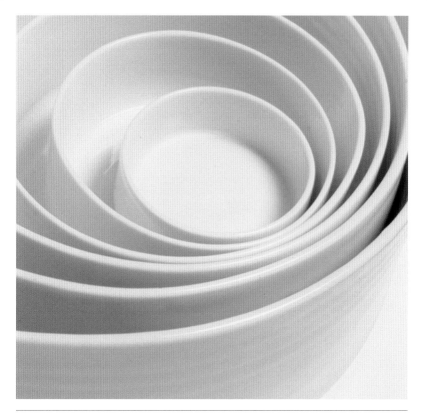

Karen Downing

Karen Downing throws porcelain pots for use. After gaining a BA from Georgetown University in Washington DC, she served two apprenticeships with potters on the east coast of America. She moved to the UK in 1985, set up her first studio in London in 1994 and now lives and works on the Suffolk coast. Her work has been shown in the UK, Europe, Japan and the USA and is included in many private collections. She is on the Crafts Council Index of Selected Makers and is represented in the Craft Council's collection.

Richmond House, Gedgrave, Orford, Suffolk, IP12 2BU Tel/Fax 01394 450313
Email karen.downing@virgin.net Visitors welcome by appontment

Bridget Drakeford

Porcelain. Wheel-thrown oriental inspired
forms, specialising in celadon and copper red
glazes. Well-established studio in beautiful
Wye Valley. Exhibits widely in UK and
abroad. Award winner in Korea and Japan.

Upper Buckenhill Farmhouse, Fownhope, Herefordshire, HR1 4PU Tel 01432 860411
Email bdrakeford@bdporcelain.co.uk Website www.bdporcelain.co.uk Visitors welcome by appointment

The Ceramics Book | 78

Georgina Dunkley

Georgina was born in 1971 and graduated from Harrow (University of Westminster) in 1996. She first discovered clay sixteen years ago and has always been captivated by its ability to hold forms and textures. Enjoying handbuilding and throwing, she combines both methods in her range of lighting. Elegant curved bases are free-formed by hand from a single sheet of clay. Shades are delicately thrown and altered, the elliptical rim echoing the soft curves of the body. She is currently developing a range of bowls, platters and tiles.

g **G**

The Chocolate Factory, Farleigh Place, London, N16 7SX Tel 020 7690 8500
Email email@georginadunkley.com Website www.georginadunkley.com Visitors welcome by appointment

Sarah Dunstan

I established a studio in St Ives, Cornwall, in 1992 after graduating from Cardiff Institute of HE, and I am now working in the Gaolyard Studios from which eight other potters also work. I decorate rolled out sheets of clay using various techniques including painting and printing with coloured slips. The pieces are then put together using paper templates to create the final form. I am fascinated by collections of objects: from the very small and personal (scent bottles) and the mundane (sardine tins) to large architectural forms (such as Gaudì buildings). Some pieces are purely ornamental while others tell a story.

Gaolyard Studios, Dove Street, St Ives, Cornwall, TR26 2LZ Tel 01736 799336 or 01736 798928 (Evening)
Email sarahdunstanceramics@hotmail.com Website www.sarahdunstan.co.uk Visitors welcome by appointment

Phyllis Dupuy

Having attended McGill University in Montreal, I spent some time teaching art in northern Ontario, where my skills as a potter were developed. I came to London in 1979, specialising in finely thrown porcelain bowls and vases. My fascination with pattern, colour relationships and textural contrasts has led to the use of complex decorating techniques involving wax resist, sgraffito and application of gold leaf and lustre. I use an electric kiln. The work has been widely exhibited in the UK and abroad, and can be found in public and private collections here and in Canada, the United States, Japan and the Middle East.

Phyllis Dupuy

48 Drayton Gardens, London, SW10 9SA Tel 020 7373 4903
Email phyllisdupuy@yahoo.co.uk Website www.phyllisdupuy.co.uk

Geoffrey Eastop Fellow

Trained as a painter at Goldsmiths College, London and at Academie Ranson, Paris. He continues to use a personal handbuilding technique to make work which is predominately sculptural in form, often using vitreous slips with painterly techniques to provide a unifying surface. Exhibited widely in Britain and abroad. Architectural commissions include large murals for Maudsley Hospital, London; Reading Civic Centre; wall and floor tiles for Robinson College Chapel, Cambridge. Work in numerous public collections including: National Museum of Wales; Fitzwilliam Museum, Cambridge; Victoria and Albert Museum, London. Principal galleries showing work: Osborne Samuel Gallery, London; Bohun Gallery, Henley on Thames. Books: *The Hollow Vessel* (Bohun Gallery, 1980) and *Geoffrey Eastop: A Potter in Practice* by Margot Coatts (1999).

The Old Post Office, Ecchinswell, Newbury, Berkshire, RG20 4TT Tel 01635 298220
Email geastop@waitrose.com Website www.bsgart.com

Sandra Eastwood

Studied sculpture at Gloucestershire College
of Art and Design (Dip AD, 1972), then
ceramics at the Royal College of Art (MA RCA,
1976). Home and workshop in Teddington.
Makes highly-fired and coloured handbuilt
forms. Pieces are made to commission and
for exhibitions. Work in private collections
worldwide.

The Bungalow, 34 Hampton Road, Teddington, TW11 0JW Tel 020 8286 4327
Email sandraeastwood@blueyonder.co.uk Website www.studiopottery.co.uk
Workshop not open to the public. Trade enquiries welcome

Victoria and Michael Eden Fellows

Since starting to work together in 1981 we have striven to make pots that combine the best traditional qualities with a modern sensibility. We make an increasing proportion of larger, individual wood-fired pieces. Many shops and galleries in the UK and abroad are supplied, including Contemporary Ceramics in London. Classes are held throughout the year including a one week slipware and wood firing course. We enjoy giving lectures and demonstrations and are authors of various articles and the book *Slipware: Contemporary Approaches* (A&C Black, 1999). Winner of the Conran Foundation Donald Potter Prize, 2005.

eden

Parkside, Hale, Milnthorpe, Cumbria, LA7 7BL Tel 01539 562342 Email mike@edenceramics.co.uk
Website www.edenceramics.co.uk Visitors welcome, opening times normally Mon-Sat 11am-5pm
but please telephone first; see website for details

Libby Edmondson

Libby Edmondson's work reflects an interest in animal forms. Some of the modelling is realistic whilst other work is more stylised. Each piece is individually modelled. Current work includes hares, goats, sheep, geese, hens and dalmations. New designs are being added all the time, often following a long gestation period and considerable experimentation. All work is made from high-fired (1250°C) craft crank clay and T material.

Where colour is used it is usually provided by high firing coloured slips or occasionally from matt glaze. The pieces are finished with an oxide wash.

Quaggs House Farm, Levens, Kendal, Cumbria, LA8 8PA Tel 01539 561546
Email nigel.libby@uk4free.net Website www.nigelandlibbyceramics.co.uk Visitors welcome by appointment

Nigel Edmondson

Nigel Edmondson's current work includes both sculptural and functional garden and conservatory pieces and some decorative domestic ware. Some of his most recent output has been an exploration of multiple and modular approaches to garden planters and some larger-scale work, including water features, particularly for a garden setting. Craft crank and T material are used, fired to 1250°C in oxidation. Only limited use is made of glazes, with colour coming, in the main, from metal oxides and high firing slips. Surfaces are either textural or incorporate landscape-based abstraction that reflects and responds in particular to the Lakeland Fells that lie on his doorstep. On occasion multiple firings are employed to allow for further refinement of the 'painted' surface.

Quaggs House Farm, Levens, Kendal, Cumbria, LA8 8PA Tel 01539 561546
Email nigel.libby@uk4free.net Website www.nigelandlibbyceramics.co.uk Visitors welcome by appointment

Ross Emerson

Trained at Loughborough College of Art, followed by eighteen months at Dartington Pottery Training Workshop. Opened his present workshop and showroom near Hemyock in the Blackdown Hills in 1990 and at the same time changed from throwing and stoneware to handbuilding and red earthenware. With an emphasis on colourful and quirky, his work encompasses a variety of one-off pieces; in particular, clocks, candelabra and vases.

Pieces are decorated using a combination of slips, underglaze colours and occasionally gold lustres.

Old Trickey's Farm House, Blackborough, Cullompton, Devon, EX15 2HZ
Email rossemerson@talktalk.net Website www.rossemerson.co.uk

Kirsti Buhler Fattorini

I was born in Winterthur, Switzerland, being fortunate to be brought up in a community where the visual arts were highly regarded. On completing formal education I studied painting and ceramics in Rome, making handbuilt earthenware pots decorated with bright abstract designs. On marrying and moving to England I was unable to find my usual materials and changed to stoneware thrown pots which I continue to decorate with abstract designs. More recently I have included slip-cast stoneware dishes suitable for domestic use. I particularly enjoy decorating and experimenting with glazes. Currently my designs are drawn from nature – animals, birds, fish and flowers.

5 Broadway, Hale, Cheshire, WA15 0PF Tel 0161 980 4504
Website www.kirstifattorini.com Visitors welcome by appointment

Sotis Filippides

Trained at the Athens College of Ceramics
and moved to London in the early 1980s. His
work is thrown in crank clay and the simplicity of the shape is the priority. He uses
different oxides to achieve matt rough surfaces and a natural organic look. Sotis's
inspiration for the shapes and texture is
drawn from nature (trees, dry leaves and
roots).

Studio IV8, Cooper House, 2 Michael Road, London, SW6 2AD Tel 020 7582 0980
Mobile 07733 151276 Email sotis@sotis.co.uk Website www.sotis.co.uk

Ray Finch Honorary Fellow

Ray Finch is one of Britain's most respected potters at home and overseas. He has been working at the Winchcombe Pottery since 1936, first under Michael Cardew and then as master potter since 1946. He still makes pots but has a free range to make what he wants these days since semi-retiring and handing over the running of the Winchcombe Pottery to his son, Mike. The team (Mike Finch, Eddie Hopkins, Dave Wilson and trainees) still makes a full range of pots for use in the home, fired to stoneware temperature in a wood-fired kiln at surprisingly low prices.

Winchcombe Pottery, Broadway Road, Winchcombe, Cheltenham, Gloucestershire, GL54 5NU
Tel 01242 602462 Email mike@winchcombepottery.co.uk Website www.winchcombepottery.co.uk

The Ceramics Book | 90

Judith Fisher

Born in Brighton. Studied Fine Art and Illustration at Brighton College of Art, followed by a year at Goldsmiths College, London, where she first became interested in ceramics. She specialises in making individual small-scale bowls and vases fired by the raku process, in which the pot is withdrawn from the red-hot kiln to be plunged into sawdust or other organic matter. When the surface has been coated with powdered copper, unpredictable colours from purple to turquoise and pink emerge. On other pieces bare clay receives interesting marks and veining from being fumed in stable sweepings.

Huntswood, St Helena's Lane, Streat, Nr Hassocks, Sussex, BN6 8SD
Tel 01273 890088 Visitors welcome by appointment

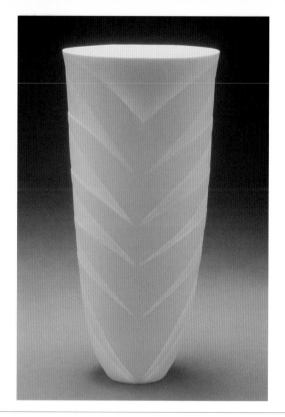

Penny Fowler

My work is individually made using bone china and porcelain clays. My interest is in exploring carving, light, shade and translucency through the interplay between form and decoration. Inspiration draws mainly from landscape, natural forms and the human body. The finished work is vitrified in an electric kiln and finely sanded to achieve a natural pebble-like quality. I sell through galleries and to private collectors from my workshop in my home, which I set up in 1984.

84 Middleton Road, Hackney, London, E8 4LN Tel 020 7254 2707
Email penny.fowler@macunlimited.net Visitors welcome by appointment

Alan Foxley

Trained at Corsham. Following a career teaching art in schools and ceramics in colleges he set up his workshop as a full-time potter in 1977. Current themes have evolved from 1997. All works are one-offs, mainly coiled using crank clay with the addition of porcelain, oxides and matt glazes and fired to 1280°C in a reducing atmosphere, and in some cases polished post-firing with abrasives. Ideas are developed from natural and man-made forms. Textures and the apparent effects of the elements and time upon the forms are of paramount importance to achieve a timeless contemplative feeling. Scale varies, but is generally large and is principally suited to outdoor display.

ALAN FOXLEY
Alan Foxley

26 Shepherds Way, Saffron Walden, Essex, CB10 2AH Tel 01799 522631
Email foxleyalan1@waitrose.com Website www.studiopottery.co.uk Visitors welcome by appointment

David Frith Fellow

Born 1943. Worked in north Wales since 1963 making mainly thrown, pressed or slabbed wood-fired reduction stoneware, often on a large scale. Uses glazed surfaces with wax motifs in combination with unglazed ashed areas. Fellow and past Vice Chairman of the CPA and member of the Crafts Council Index of Selected Makers. Exhibited and worked abroad, especially Japan. Work in private and public collections at home and abroad including Victoria and Albert Museum. Organiser of *ClayArt Wales*, now in its fifth year.

Brookhouse Pottery, Brookhouse Lane, Denbigh, Denbighshire, LL16 4RE
Tel/Fax 01745 812805 Email frith@brookhousepottery.co.uk Website www.brookhousepottery.co.uk

Margaret Frith Fellow

Born 1943 and works in North Wales making
reduction porcelain personal pieces.
Decorative techniques include wax and lay-
ered glazes, freely drawn brushwork, ashed
surfaces or celadon glazes over carved motifs.
Worked and exhibited abroad especially
Japan. Work in private and public collections
at home and abroad. Council Member CPA and
new membership officer. Organises annual
ClayArt Wales with David.

Brookhouse Pottery, Brookhouse Lane, Denbigh, Denbighshire, LL16 4RE
Tel/Fax 01745 812805 Email frith@brookhousepottery.co.uk Website www.brookhousepottery.co.uk

Tessa Fuchs Fellow

Born Knutsford, Cheshire. Studied Salford
Royal Technical College Art School, and
Central School of Arts and Crafts, London.
Set up studio as an individual artist potter
making sculptural pieces and some domestic
ware in high-fired earthenware using colourful matt glazes. Work inspired by animals,
trees, plants, landscape, gardens and the
human form. Particularly influenced by travels, which have included China, Mexico,
Africa and India. The work has an element
of fantasy and humour. Now painting larger
than life, brilliantly colourful portraits in
oils, as well as potting.

Trinity Cottage, Chediston, Halesworth, Suffolk, IP19 0AT Tel 01986 875724
Visitors welcome by appointment

Liz Gale Fellow

I trained as a teacher, specialising in textile arts, and taught in primary schools for ten years, dividing my time between teaching and ceramics. I gave up teaching and became a full-time potter in 1988, moving into a purpose-built workshop and showroom in 1992. My early work focused on domestic reduction stoneware, decorated using latex, sponge, trailing and wax resist. In 2001 I built a 30 cubic foot salt kiln, again producing domestic ware and individual pieces. Having served in various capacities on the Craft Potters Association Council for some fifteen years, I am currently a Trustee and the Secretary to the Craft Potters Charitable Trust. My main source of inspiration as a potter is my enjoyment of food. Good pots should be used for good food and drink.

Taplands Farm Cottage, Webbs Green, Soberton, Southampton, Hampshire, SO32 3PY
Tel 023 9263 2686 Email lizgale@interalpha.co.uk Visitors welcome by appointment

Tony Gant Fellow

Makes stoneware bowls, dishes, plates, jugs,
mugs and vases. Established 1961; present
studio since 1968. Student of the late
Gwilym Thomas.

Tim Gee

Exploring light through the medium of translucent thrown porcelain. I use etching to modify the vessel, adding texture and simultaneously allowing light and colour to permeate and activate the form, casting shadows and softening the boundary between interior and exterior space. I aim for a high level of craftsmanship, with throwing as both working method and inspiration. Crafts Council's Index of Selected Makers. Member of the Devon Guild of Craftsmen and the Society of Designer Craftsmen.

165 Grenville Road, Plymouth, Devon, PL4 9QD Tel 01752 225120 Email tim@timgeeceramics.co.uk
Website www.timgeeceramics.co.uk Workshop open by arrangement

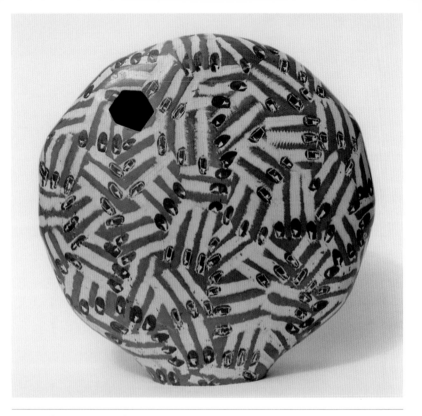

Carolyn Genders Fellow

Carolyn Genders makes individual handbuilt, coiled or press-moulded pieces, built from white earthenware clay using burnished or vitreous slips to create surface pattern and texture. Mainly vessel-based – the asymmetric sculptural forms explore the relationship of form to surface. She is intrigued by the three-dimensionality of form and how it is visually altered by the addition of surface texture or pattern that emphasises nuance of shape and creates mood and atmosphere. She exhibits extensively throughout the UK and overseas and her work is represented in many private and public collections including Cologne Museum, Brighton and Hove Museum and The Fine Arts Society, Glasgow. She regularly gives lectures and demonstrations. Author of *Sources of Inspiration* (A&C Black, 2002).

Oak Farm, Lewes Road, Danehill, East Sussex, RH17 7HD Tel 01825 790575
Email carolyn.genders@boltblue.com Website www.carolyngenders.co.uk Visitors welcome by appointment

Christine Gittens

South African born and educated, Christine Gittins moved to Wales in 1994 where she set up a studio in the historical hilltop town of Llantrisant. Using the potter's wheel she throws her rounded vessels, elongated bottles and wide-rimmed bowls. The pieces are smoothly burnished and fired in a saggar with copper, salt and sawdust to achieve the unique finish that distinguishes her work. Inspiration is drawn from various sources:

African clay pots, classical pots from ancient European and Eastern civilizations and minimalist modernism. Her work is shown in select galleries in Britain, South Africa and France. The Old Bakehouse Pottery Studio and Gallery houses both her showroom and workshop. It also has a unique selection of work for sale by artists and craft makers from Britain, South Africa and the continent, selected by Christine to reflect her own interests and preferences.

The Old Bakehouse Studio and Gallery, 7A Swan Street, Llantrisant, Mid Glamorgan, CF72 8ED
Tel 01443 225899 Email christinegittins@aol.com Open Wed-Sat 11am-5pm, Sun 2-5pm
Please telephone first if making a special journey

Richard Godfrey Fellow

I trained at Bristol, graduating in 1972 and opened my first full-time studio in 1980 in Devon, making domestic ware. My current work is a mixture of both thrown and hand-built forms. I use a white earthenware body with additions of molochite for larger pieces. The work is decorated with a range of coloured slips which are sprayed, brushed, sponged and trailed over wax and paper resists. Glaze firing is to 1140°C in oxida-

tion. The inspiration for my forms and decoration comes from the beautiful coastline and countryside around my studio. New work includes a series of large landscape forms using new glazes and firing techniques. I sell my work throughout Europe and have been guest demonstrator at many international events and seminars. I served for three years on the CPA council. For more information visit my website.

1 Battisborough Cross, Holbeton, Nr Plymouth, Devon, PL8 1JT Tel 01752 830457
Email rg@richardgodfreyceramics.co.uk Website www.richardgodfreyceramics.co.uk Visitors welcome

Christopher Green Fellow

Formulates his own porcelain body to make
plates, bowls and sculptures that are fired to
1300°C in a reduction atmosphere. Born and
educated in Zimbabwe. Trained in Durban,
South Africa in the early 1970s and then at
Goldsmiths' College in the early 1980s. He
has developed software to formulate glazes
which can be downloaded from
www.glazecalc.com.

PO Box 115, Westbury-on-Trym, Bristol, BS9 3ND Tel 0117 950 0852
Email cguk@seegreen.com Visitors welcome by appointment

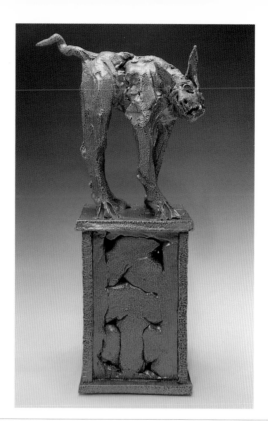

Ian Gregory Fellow

Workshop opened in 1968, producing ceramic sculpture. Elected to Craft Potters Association in 1977, and served on the council for two years. Wrote *Kiln Building* in 1977, followed by *Sculptural Ceramic* and *Alternative Kilns*. His work is shown in galleries worldwide and in public and private collections including the Victoria and Albert Museum. Visiting lecturer at many art schools in the UK and around the world. Currently producing one-off pieces for exhibitions and public commissions.

The Studio, Crumble Cottage, Ansty, Dorchester, Dorset, DT2 7PN Tel/Fax 01258 880891
Email igreg891@aol.com or ian@ian-gregory.co.uk Website www.ian-gregory.co.uk
Workshop and studio open 2-6pm weekdays, 9am-6pm weekends, or by arrangement

Barry Guppy

Barry was born in the Channel Island of Jersey in 1937 where he and his family were prisoners of war from 1939-45. He was taught by Hans Coper and Dame Lucie Rie and later taught alongside them at Camberwell School of Art for some twelve years part-time. Barry Guppy has exhibited extensively in this country and abroad whilst having annual shows at his Pimlico pottery in central London from 1967 until 2003. Since 1975 his ceramics were being made from a specially adjusted porcelain casting lip in a process of spinning and drawing that he invented. He is now working in a very beautiful part of the New Forest National Park near Brockenhurst, Hampshire.

154A Southbourne Overcliff Drive, Bournemouth, Dorset, BH6 3NH
Tel 01202 425495 (Home) Tel 01590 624911 (Studio) Mobile 07986 744850
Email barry.guppy@btinternet.com Website www.barryguppy.co.uk

Jennifer Hall

Jennifer Hall graduated from Cardiff in 1994. She has a studio near Rhayader in mid Wales where she pots on a kickwheel, making slip-decorated, useable earthenware. The pots are available from galleries and pottery fairs or directly from Jennifer.

Spring Gardens, Llanwrthwl, Llandrindod Wells, Powys, LD1 6NU Tel 01597 810119
Email jennythepotter@hotmail.com Visitors welcome by appointment

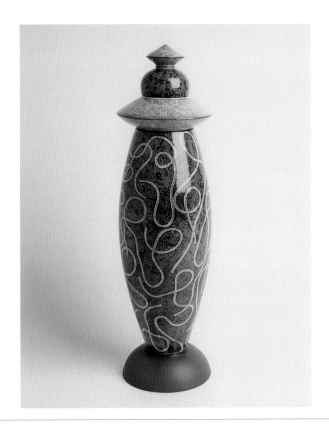

Morgen Hall Fellow

Makes a wide range of domestic tableware
which is inspired by the food it is intended
for, from tea cabaret sets to spaghetti jars.
Most of the work is wheel-thrown and
turned from tin-glazed red earthenware. A
new range is also being made from soda
fired porcelain. For further information see
the website.

Chapter Arts Centre, Market Road, Canton, Cardiff, CF5 1QE
Tel 029 2031 1050 ext 219 or 029 2023 8716 Website www.morgenhall.co.uk Visitors welcome by appointment

The Ceramics Book | 107

Janet Halligan

I graduated from Stourbridge College of Art
in 1970 with Dip AD Hons. I make *trompe
l'oeil* sculptures and handbuilt vessels fea-
turing different kinds of fastenings. I work
in stoneware using a range of glazes and
metal lustres to achieve a realistic effect.

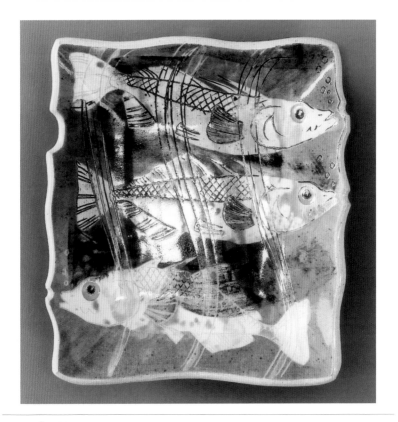

Frank Hamer Honorary Fellow

Press-moulded plates and dishes which are decorated, often on the back as well, with graphic images taken from nature. The ware is reduced stoneware and all pieces have integral hangers for wall display or can be used as servers. Frank Hamer lives in rural Wales, working in a studio which overlooks the Brecon Canal and where studio and kiln space are shared with Janet Hamer. He is co-author of *Clays* (Pitman) and *The Potter's Dictionary of Materials and Techniques* (A&C Black).

Llwyn-On, Croes-yn-y-Pant, Mamhilad, Pontypool, NP4 8RE
Tel 01495 785700 Visitors welcome by appointment

Mohamed Hamid

Mohamed Hamid completed a BA Hons degree in ceramics in 1983 at Farnham Art College, West Surrey. He was then fortunate to train with Alan Caiger-Smith and Edgar Campden at the Aldermaston Pottery from 1983-6. From there Mohamed moved to Sussex to work with Jonathan Chiswell-Jones for three years. In 1989 he set up his own workshop in Lewes, East Sussex with a Crafts Council Grant. Mohamed makes brush deco-rated, hand-thrown, stoneware pottery in the tin-glazed earthenware tradition. His work is influenced by Islamic art, continental majoli-ca and Dutch delftware. Mohamed makes lim-ited editions, one-off pieces and private commissions, which include inscribed plates, bowls, mugs, tankards, jugs and house plates. These make ideal gifts for anniver-saries, weddings, births, christenings, birth-days and all occasions.

Star Gallery Pottery, Fisher Street, Lewes, East Sussex, BN7 1YJ Tel 01273 483295
Mobile 07843 287187 Email info@mohamedhamid-pottery.co.uk Website www.mohamedhamid-pottery.co.uk

Jane Hamlyn Fellow

Saltglaze pots for use and ornament. Work
in public collections: Victoria and Albert
Museum; Crafts Council, London; Nottingham
Castle Museum; Hanley Museum, Stoke on
Trent; Warttembergisches Landsmuseum,
Stuttgart etc.

Millfield Pottery, Everton, Nr Doncaster, South Yorkshire, DN10 5DD
Tel 01777 817723 Visitors welcome by appointment

Lisa Hammond Fellow

Born 1956, I have worked as a potter in
London since 1979. Vapour glazing since college, first using salt and since the early 1980s,
with soda glaze. I produce a range of functional ware for the preparation, cooking and
serving of food. It is immensely important to
me that this work is used in daily life.
Alongside functional ware I have always made
a range of work that is more individual and
playful, but more recently I have developed a
larger amount of this work and now divide my
time evenly between the two. In 2003/4 I
spent three months making and firing in the
Mino area for several exhibitions in Japan. I
have always used shino as a liner glaze for the
functional range and I am now in the process
of finding my own voice with shino. I have
lectured and exhibited widely, and my work is
represented in museums and collections both
in the UK and abroad, including Japan.

Maze Hill Pottery, The Old Ticket Office, Woodlands Park Road, Greenwich, London, SE10 9XE
Tel/Fax 020 8293 0048 Email mazehill.pottery@virgin.net Website www.mazehill-pottery.com
Visitors welcome by appointment; students with genuine interest in soda glaze accepted for work placements

Ashraf Hanna Fellow

Born in Egypt, 1967. Originally trained in
Theatre Design at Central St Martins
College of Art and Design, London, 1991-4.
Discovered clay in 1997. Makes individual,
handbuilt, burnished vessels. Linear
designs are achieved through naked raku.
Current areas of interest include vessel-
based sculptural forms and further exploration of surface treatments.

ASH

Pen-y-Daith, Chapel Lane, Keeston, Haverfordwest, Pembrokeshire, SA62 6EH Tel 01437 710774
Email ashrafhanna.ceramics@btinternet.com Visitors welcome by appointment

Keiko Harada

Originally from Japan, Keiko obtained a BA Art and Design at Leeds Metropolitan University in 1999. Oriental influences are strong in her work, which springs from her long involvement with Japanese calligraphy and textiles. She expresses her feeling for nature and the human spirit in an abstract way, using calligraphy brushes to emphasise the spontaneous movement of line. Her works have been selected by international competitions such as the Fletcher Challenge Ceramics Award, New Zealand, the Mashiko International Pottery Contest and Mino in Japan. She exhibits in the UK and abroad, and was invited to attend the International Summer Workshops in Zlakusa, Serbia (2003-4) and in Tokoname, Japan (2005). Her work is handbuilt, slab construction, textured, often slip-painted before assembly, porcelain and T material (50/50), 1260°C oxidation.

Park Lea, 36 West Park Crescent, Roundhay, Leeds, LS8 2EQ
Tel/Fax 0113 266 3462 Email keiko17@ntlworld.com Visitors welcome by appointment

Rebecca Harvey

Rebecca Harvey's highly individual pieces combine elegance with function. Initially inspired by the traditions of Oriental ceramics and eighteenth-century English creamware. Contemporary designs have developed to include distinctive details of twisted handles and elongated spouts. Each piece of tableware in the range is finely hand thrown and includes teapots, coffeepots, jugs, mugs and bowls. The introduction of sodium carbonate during the firing process gives the characteristic orange peel surface. This alluring tactile effect becomes part of the body of the pot making each piece unique.

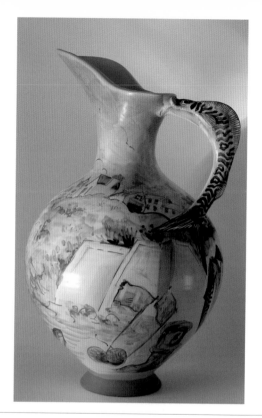

Michael and Barbara Hawkins Fellows

Michael and Barbara Hawkins live and work in the picturesque fishing village of Port Isaac in north Cornwall, where Michael grew up. Their workshop and showroom is in a converted Methodist chapel and home is in the Sunday school overlooking the harbour. Since moving back to Cornwall the pottery has become more influenced by the themes of the sea and fishing. The pottery is stoneware, with extensive use of lustres and precious metals, fired in a 50 cubic foot oil-fired kiln.

Port Issac Pottery, The Old Chapel, Roscarrock Hill, Port Issac, Cornwall, PL29 3RG
Tel/Fax 01208 880625 Open Apr-Oct: daily 10am-4pm; Nov-Mar: Thurs-Sun only

Peter Hayes Fellow

I have always been interested in why and how 'things' are made of clay. I am naturally drawn to shapes of artefacts and objects from other cultures and other times, but that remain timeless. Erosion and change through time and nature are recorded in a piece. My main aim in my work is not to compete with nature; but for the work to evolve within the environment. The minerals, like iron and copper, that I introduce into the raku ceramic surface have their own effect on the clay during the time they are submerged in the river or the sea. This erosion process continues with sanding so that the texture and cracks do not interrupt the surface but become an organic, integral part of the patina. Each individual piece takes on its own developing surface; its own history and its own aesthetic. I am merely the maker.

2 Cleveland Bridge, Bath, BA1 5DH Tel/Fax 01225 466215
Email phayesceramics@aol.com Website www.peterhayes-ceramics.com Visitors welcome by appointment

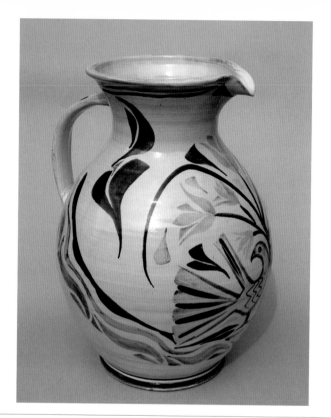

Andrew Hazelden

Trained in ceramics at Epsom Art School 1981-4. After leaving Epsom he joined Alan Caiger-Smith and the team of potters at the Aldermaston Pottery. There he learnt the technique of tin-glazed earthenware, making and painting Aldermaston shapes and patterns for nine years up to the closure of the pottery in May 1993. Andrew then became independent, and he now works in the old workshop at Aldermaston producing domestic and commemorative tin-glazed earthenware. He sells from the showroom there and occasionally has exhibitions in galleries.

The Pottery, The Street, Aldermaston, Berkshire, RG7 4LW Tel 0118 971 3359
Email andrew@haze004.freeserve.co.uk Website www.studiopottery.co.uk

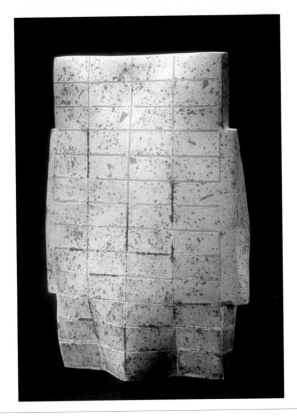

Regina Heinz Fellow

Regina Heinz produces fine art ceramics for interior and exterior spaces. Constructed from soft slabs of clay, the undulating forms of her sculptures and wall panels display an organic quality but are essentially abstract in dealing with line, form, volume and colour. Geometric designs are used as a starting point and transformed by the sensual quality of clay to create aesthetic objects that address both our visual and tactile experience. Regina studied painting and ceramics in Vienna, Geneva and London (Goldsmiths College), where she established her studio in 1996. Received a Crafts Council Setting Up Grant in 1998. Regina has won national and international awards for her ceramics and her work has been purchased by various museums such as the Fitzwilliam Museum in Cambridge and the Potteries Museum and Art Gallery in Stoke-on-Trent.

Home: 52 Culmstock Road, London, SW11 6LU Tel/Fax 020 7738 0813
Studio: Studio 213E, Wandsworth Business Village, Broomhill Road, London, SW18 4JQ Tel 020 8871 5118
Email regina_heinz@ceramart.net Website www.ceramart.net

Rick Henham

Presently makes black and white glazed
stoneware vases that are thrown and
turned. Stainless steel wire embellishment
post firing. Allusions to classical form with
a contemporary design appeal. Trained at
the University of Westminster, Harrow
(1993-6). Other fields of work have included jewellery making, antique restoration,
therapeutic massage, garden design and
construction. Until recently based in

London with a studio at the Chocolate
Factory, Hackney. Now lives in Cornwall
with shared workspace at Gaolyard Studios,
St Ives.

Home: 2B Chy-an-Hall, Gulval, Penzance, Cornwall, TR18 3LY Tel 01736 332377
Studio: Gaolyard Studios, Dove Street, St Ives, Cornwall, TR26 2LZ Mobile 07880 794544
Email info@rickhenham.com Website www.rickhenham.com

André Hess Fellow

Makes abstracted and elusive shapes that require the viewer to question what they mean rather than puzzle over what they resemble or represent. The work is simultaneously familiar and fugitive, but always evocative of the history and theory of clay. It resists immediate reading and is firmly positioned in the wider world of made objects. The handling of the clay informs the meaning of the work. He uses any technique that fulfils the requirement. Surface treatment only qualifies what is already there, and is achieved using slips, oxides and frits. Awards include *Ceramic Review* Award and CPA Award, 1993; Judge's Commendation, Fletcher Challenge, New Zealand, 1996; Sculpture Award, Altech International Biennale, Johannesburg, 2000; Awards of Honour, World Ceramics Exposition, Korea, 2001 and 2003. Recently selected to EuCeCo 04 and CERCO 05.

32 Seaman Close, Park Street, St Albans, Hertfordshire, AL2 2NX Tel 01727 874299
Email andre@earthwaterfire.demon.co.uk Visitors welcome by appointment

Karin Hessenberg Fellow

I graduated from Camberwell School of Arts and Crafts in 1974. Most of my work comprises sculptural garden planters, lanterns, stools and other ornaments. My designs are inspired by Indian architecture, Peruvian textiles and plant forms. My work is handbuilt from robust craft crank stoneware clay, which is raw-glazed and high-fired to 1260°C making it resistant to frost. The stoneware pieces come in a choice of three colours: a deep blue matt ash glaze, a soft matt green and a stony white glaze. My pieces are ideal for creating a focal point in a small courtyard, patio or intimate corner of a garden. I also make a small range of pieces in semi-porcelain clay. These include slab-built dishes and candle-holders with designs based on leaves and other plant forms. Author of *Sawdust Firing* (BT Batsford Ltd, 1994) and *Ceramics for Gardens and Landscapes* (A&C Black, 2000).

72 Broomgrove Road, Sheffield, S10 2NA Tel 0114 266 1610
Email mail@karinhessenberg.co.uk Website www.karinhessenberg.co.uk Visitors welcome by appointment

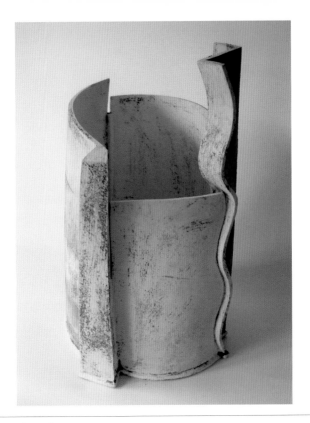

John Higgins Fellow

The shapes position themselves not only in terms of pottery but also the wider world of industrial and designed objects, as well as architecture old and new. The surfaces are achieved using a variety of oxides and slips, and serve only to complete what is already there. They recall the marks and patterns left on walls of buildings both inhabited and abandoned. A basic vessel shape is planned, but the spontaneous and expressive possibilities of the clay itself are always encouraged. The technique follows the idea, and wheel-thrown and slabbed elements are frequently juxtaposed. The fired objects vary in size from something hand-held to pieces fit for large spaces.

JH

32 Seaman Close, Park Street, St Albans, Hertfordshire, AL2 2NX Tel 01727 874299
Email johnceramics@aol.com Visitors welcome by appointment

Andrew Hill Fellow

Born in 1964 in Beaconsfield,
Buckinghamshire. After completing his
Diploma in Ceramics at Derby Lonsdale in
1985, he began working as a potter in his
own studio and workshop in Trawden,
Lancashire. The influence of eastern ceramics led him to specialise in thrown work as
well as the techniques of raku firing.
Works with a variety of materials during
the reduction including bracken, ferns and
sawdust. The result is a dramatic contrast
of vibrant, spontaneous colour against a
blackened, carbonised body. Work is widely
collected and exhibited throughout the UK
and Europe.

Quarry Hill Cottage, Park Lane, Carleton in Craven, Nr Skipton, North Yorkshire, BD23 3BH
Tel 01756 795787 Email andrew@hill25.fsworld.co.uk Visitors welcome by appointment

Wendy Hoare

Degree in Fine Art, Reading University, specialising in sculpture. Taught art for ten
years. Work is made completely with hand-
rolled coils of clay. The textured surfaces are
emphasised with oxides and frit. Electric
kiln, firing range 1200-1260°C.

135 Billing Road, Northampton, NN1 5RR Tel 01604 622880
Website www.studiopottery.co.uk Visitors welcome by appointment

Terri Holman

I studied ceramics at Cardiff School of Art,
graduating in 1981. For the last ten years I
have lived and worked on the edge of
Dartmoor near Bovey Tracey in Devon. The
vessels are formed from flat slabs of clay and
occupy a shallow space. I am interested in
playing with an illusory sense of volume and
depth that is emphasised with the handling
of surface pattern, texture and colour.
(Photo: Mei Lim)

TH.

Northcombe, Moretonhampstead Road, Bovey Tracey, Devon, TQ13 9NH
Tel 01626 835578 Visitors welcome by appointment

Duncan Hooson

Born Stoke-on-Trent, 1959. Trained Bristol BA 1983; Cardiff MA 1985. I produce work mainly to public or private commission and employ a wide range of ceramic techniques and scale – from high-relief murals to domestic and sculptural forms for internal or external locations. I also work as an artist-in-residence in schools, hospitals and on community projects and enjoy facilitating commissions that engage a wider public. The pots I make are always wheel-thrown and are usually made of composites, as it is the joining together and manipulation of clay that provides me with the satisfaction of the making process. I teach ceramics at Morley College in London on non-vocational courses.

9 Birchington Road, Crouch End, London, N8 8HR Tel/Fax 020 8342 9032
Email duncan.hooson@hoosonwest.demon.co.uk Visitors welcome by appointment

Harry Horlock-Stringer Fellow

Self-taught 'painter turned potter', he found a new way of understanding the formulation of glazes without the use of molecular formulae. Personally built a school which opened in 1965 and catered for an international summer school until 1998. Author of the first book on raku in the West in 1967, produced an electric raku kiln for use in the classroom in 1965. Researched the development of quality in oxidising atmospheres producing the first 'reactive slip' in 1975. CPA Council member during its first nine years and editor of the CPA journal. Workshop in Fulham Pottery in the 1950s making domestic once-fired earthenware, later transferring to Taggs Yard, London SW13, making tin-glazed earthenware. Later work in stoneware and porcelain. Exhibited at home and abroad. Head of art department in teacher training college for many years. Recently moved to Lopen, South Petherton, Somerset.

King William House, Lopen, South Petherton, Somerset, TA13 5JU
Tel/Fax 01460 242135

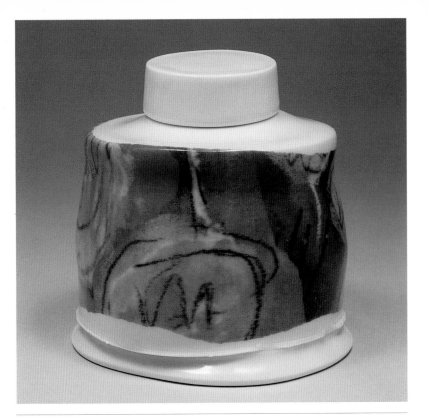

Ashley Howard Fellow

Ashley Howard lives and works in Kent. He studied at the Royal College of Art and also writes and lectures on ceramics. He produces porcelain and stoneware vessels that occupy two different areas. The first is a range of tableware informed by a dialogue between Far Eastern and homespun pottery traditions. The second body of work comprises larger, one-off pieces which draw upon his interest in ritual vessels, especially fonts, the spaces they occupy and the ceremonies that surround them. Wider issues explored in this work are location, space and narrative as well as notions of reverence and transience.

3 Albion Road, Tunbridge Wells, Kent, TN1 2PB Tel 01892 533158 Mobile 07970 424762
Email ashleyhoward@ukonline.co.uk Website www.studiopottery.co.uk Visitors welcome by appointment

Joanna Howells Fellow

My work concentrates on form and texture. I aim to make pieces which are very simple yet have a softness, a freedom and a sculptural quality. The work varies in size from small, intimate domestic ware to larger scale pieces.

2 Cwrt Isaf, Tythegston, Bridgend, Mid-Glamorgan, CF32 0ND Tel 01656 784021 or 01656 788731
Email studio@joannahowells.co.uk Website www.joannahowells.co.uk Visitors welcome by appointment

John Huggins Fellow

Maker of garden pots and ornaments, mostly
in terracotta.

Ruardean Garden Pottery, Ruardean, Forest of Dean, Gloucestershire, GL17 9TP Tel 01594 543577
Website www.ruardeanpottery.com Workshop usually open Tues-Sat 10am-4.30pm

Simon Hulbert Fellow

Simon Hulbert produces a wide range of terracotta gardenware from his studio in Hay-on-Wye. The larger pieces, usually made to commission, reflect a long-standing interest in classical form and proportion. Whilst this is an underlying theme, he takes pleasure in adopting a looser approach which exploits the softer qualities of clay. Pots are constructed using a combination of throwing, press-moulding and coiling. They are then high fired to bring out the rich colours of the clay and slips and ensure that they are frost-proof. The studio has a large gallery space which stocks contemporary British studio ceramics, furniture and sculpture for the garden.

Brook Street Pottery, Hay-on-Wye, Hereford, HR3 5BQ Tel 01497 821070
Email info@hayclay.co.uk Website www.hayclay.co.uk Studio and gallery open throughout the year

Tim Hurn

Wood-fired saltglaze. Born 1964, Moseley, Birmingham. Trained at Camberwell School of Art 1982-7. Built first wood-fired kiln in Chislehurst, Kent and exhibited at the RBSA, Birmingham, 1987-8. Attended the International Workshop of Ceramic Art in Tokoname, Japan, exhibiting at Tokoname Ceramic Festival. During 1989-91, apprentice to John Leach at Muchelney Pottery. In 1992, moved to Bettiscombe, Dorset, to build anagama kiln and establish a workshop. David Canter Memorial Fund award, 1995. I make thrown table and garden ware, as well as one-off pots which explore the more extreme effects of long anagama firings. Simple shino and wood ash glazes enhanced by rivers of 'fly-ash' and salt from brine-soaked bundles of orchard prunings.

Home Farm House, Bettiscombe, Bridport, Dorset, DT6 5NU Tel 01308 868171
Email timhurn@bettiscombe96.fsnet.co.uk Workshop open by appointment

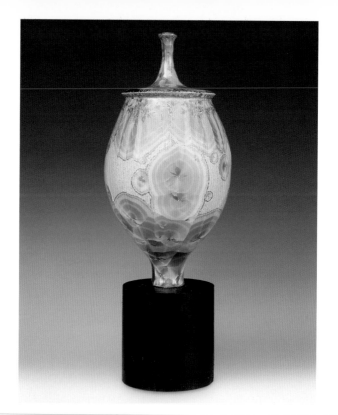

Peter Ilsley

Peter Ilsley began potting in 1963, producing domestic stoneware and one-off sculptural and decorative pieces. After moving to a new home and studio on the Grand Union Canal, Northamptonshire, in 1986, glazed, dry copper and naked raku were added to the range. In 1989, being a compulsive experimenter and masochist, he made a conscious decision to research and produce crystalline-glazed porcelain, which now takes over ninety per cent of the production time and offers a most satisfying challenge. Has been involved in a number of international exhibitions, symposia and workshops. Author of *Macro-Crystalline Glazes* (Crowood Press).

Whilton Locks Pottery, Whilton Locks, Daventry, Northamptonshire, NN11 2NH Tel/Fax 01327 842886
Website www.studiopottery.co.uk Visitors welcome by appointment

Claire Ireland

My work is handbuilt using colour and glaze to create the surface. Fragments of pattern and texture are important in the process for developing new ways of making marks, integral to the making. The images and forms are developed through sketchbook drawings and collecting visual information from contemporary sources, combining a fascination for the tribal and ceremonial aspects of past cultures. I work on different scales, making small objects, keepsakes that accompany the creatures, be it human or animal. These are often combined with fragments of stone, metal, weathered wood or fused glass. Selecting these mixed media elements is crucial to the finished piece, and the intention is to sustain an equilibrium but to leave their interpretation to the eye of the beholder.

35 Clifden Road, Brentford, Middlesex, TW8 0PB Tel 020 8568 9287
Email claireirelanduk@yahoo.co.uk Visitors welcome by appointment

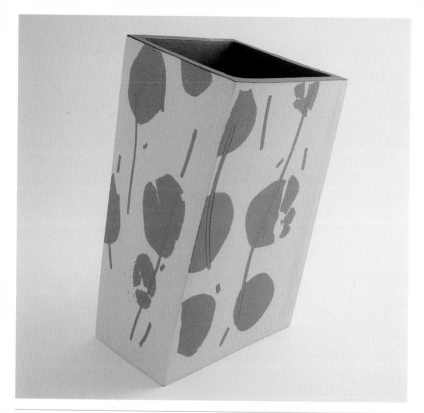

Bernard Irwin

Bernard Irwin works with clay and porcelain bodies coloured with oxides and stains. Coloured clays are shaped and collaged into soft slabs prior to forming the pieces, allowing him to compose freely and with a light touch, investing his work with freshness and spontaneity. There is a sense of immediacy, fluidity and movement. Pieces are abstract; he is more concerned with creating sensations than with illustration. Form, rhythm, movement, colour and texture are the key elements in the work. He is inspired by many things: from geology and fossils to music and poetry; the space and movement seen while snorkelling around the Cornish coast; his partner Claire's garden, which surrounds the studios at Chyenhal. His time is divided between painting and ceramics. Exhibited widely his work is in public and private collections. Commissions welcomed.

Irwin

The Barn, South Downs, Chyenhal, Nr Drift, Penzance, Cornwall, TR19 6AW Tel 01736 731899
Email studio@bernardirwin.com Website www.bernardirwin.com Visitors welcome by appointment

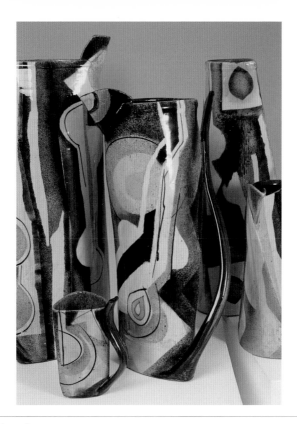

Paul Jackson Fellow

I work on a series of thrown forms, which are
altered and sculpted in terracotta. The slipped
vessels are decorated with applied, sprayed or
painted decoration, which may be polychro-
matic or monochromatic. Abstract, pictorial
and life drawing all have their part. The
emphasis is on energy and inner strength.
Recently my work has included surface textural changes to extend the interaction, especially within the abstract decorated group.

Helland Bridge Pottery, Helland Bridge, Bodmin, Cornwall, PL30 4QR Tel 01208 75240
Fax 01208 78893 Email paul@paul-jackson.co.uk Website www.paul-jackson.co.uk

Anne James Fellow

The work is made in porcelain. Some forms
are slab-built, others thrown. Coloured slips
are sprayed on and burnished while still
slightly damp. After biscuit firing, layers of
resin lustres are applied by painting, printing
and resist methods. The lustre firing is about
800°C and the pots are taken hot from the
kiln and smoked with fine sawdust. Ideas
are drawn from many sources including the
rich colours and surfaces of ethnic textiles.

Ashleigh, Gloucester Street, Painswick, Gloucester, GL6 6QN Tel 01452 813378
Email annejames@sjld.co.uk Visitors welcome by appointment

Victoria Jardine

My work is an exploration of form through the language of the vessel. A vessel exists to be filled and emptied and my pieces are made with this purpose in mind, be it flowers or thoughts. I work in stoneware at a range of scales and each piece is handbuilt, predominantly coiled. I use strong contrasts between glazes and scarification to retain the movement of making and to help describe and outline each form.

Archway Ceramics, 410 Haven Mews, 23 St Pauls Way, London, E3 4AG Tel 020 8983 1323
Email victoriajardine@hotmail.co.uk Website www.victoriajardine.com Visitors welcome by appointment

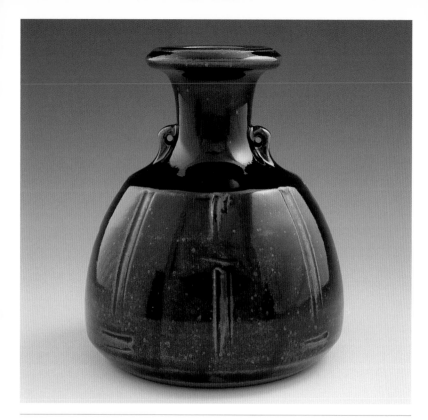

John Jelfs Fellow

Set up present studio in 1973 with my wife, Jude Jelfs. For the past few years I have been concentrating on a range of forms, to which I apply olive/celadon, ochre, temmoku and shino glazes made up from wood ash and clay, ingredients both local to my studio. Recently I have built a soda kiln and am increasingly encouraged by the results. I dislike clutter and over-elaboration. My aim has always been to make simple, heart-felt work.

Cotswold Pottery, Clapton Row, Bourton-on-the-Water, Cheltenham, Gloucestershire, GL54 2DN
Tel/Fax 01451 820173 Email pots@cotswoldpottery.co.uk Website www.cotswoldpottery.co.uk
Showroom open Mon-Sat 9.30am-5pm, Sun 10.30am-5pm

Jude Jelfs

I studied fine art but became a potter when I
married John Jelfs. Over the past few years, I
have returned to my roots, combining pottery
with drawing, painting and sculpture. My
work starts with life drawing and is an exten-
sion of this. I am interested in the human figure and the anthropomorphic qualities of pottery forms. My work is sold through leading
galleries in the UK, the USA and Canada, as
well as from our showroom in the Cotswolds.

Jude Jelfs

JUDE
JELFS

Cotswold Pottery, Clapton Row, Bourton-on-the-Water, Cheltenham, Gloucestershire, GL54 2DN
Tel/Fax 01451 820173 Email pots@cotswoldpottery.co.uk Website www.cotswoldpottery.co.uk
Showroom open Mon-Sat 9.30am-5pm, Sun 10.30am-5pm

Chris Jenkins Fellow

As a student I started as a sculptor and painter, first at Harrogate then at the Slade school. Bill Newland encouraged a serious interest in ceramics and I continued with another year at the Central school. Since then I have worked in production potteries and taught as a lecturer besides producing my own work. At present I make a range of thrown pieces in oxidised stoneware with a continuing theme of asymmetric geometry.

Surface treatments include overlaid glazes as well as engraved, inlaid and masked slips. In the summer I make functional wood-fired stoneware at my pottery in France.

Linda John

I was born in Edinburgh in 1950 and studied
art and design at Grays School of Art,
Aberdeen, Scotland. I now live in Wales, and
make large stoneware urns and mixed media
wall sculptures.

Ty Llwyd, Dyffryn Ardudwy, Gwynedd, LL44 2EP Tel 01341 247580
Email lindajohn@mac.com Website www.lindajohn.co.uk

Wendy Johnson Fellow

Having graduated from Derbyshire College of Higher Education in 1990 I spent two years as an artist-in-residence at a Nottingham secondary school, developing my work, exhibiting and selling throughout the UK. I moved my studio to my home in Nottingham until 1996. I now work from home in Derbyshire, concentrating on educational work and developing my range. Each piece is handbuilt, drawing inspiration from many sources including architecture, textiles and more recently stories and illustration. Through recent travels and work in education I am continuously finding new inspirations. I use Studio White earthenware to slab, pinch and model. Body stains and oxides are used to obtain vibrant colour and contrast, firing to 1100°C. My range includes decorative clocks, candlesticks, bowls, vessels, cheese platters, butter dishes and lidded boxes with birds and fish.

8 Cromford Road, Wirksworth, Derbyshire, DE4 4FH Tel 01629 822061
Email wendyjohnsonceramics@hotmail.com Visitors welcome by appointment

Emma Johnstone

Emma Johnstone makes thrown double-walled bowls and vessels that are raku-fired and gilded with precious metals. Set up studio in 1996 supplying work to galleries throughout the UK and Europe. Current work is focused on the deconstruction of her forms, and use of different textures and smoking techniques.

The Blue Door Studio, c/o 34 Hawks Road, Kingston upon Thames, Surrey, KT1 3EG
Tel 020 8549 7670 Mobile 07970 672535 Email embluedoor@aol.com Visitors welcome by appointment

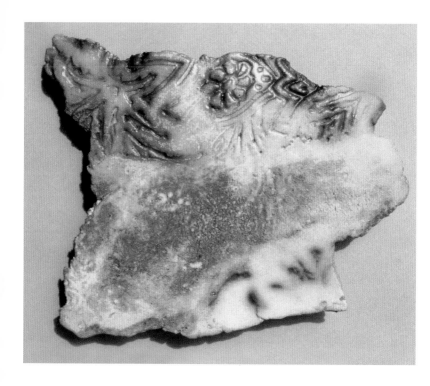

Philip Jolley

Originally from Stoke-on-Trent, where I
trained (1974-7), I moved to Oxford in 1993
and set up my present workshop. Work continues to be linked to the idea of many sides
and viewing points, with smooth and textured areas, vivid and sombre colours, all
combined to create striking forms often
incorporating mosaic-like decoration. Recent
pieces use this surface decoration to create
wall panels with an archaeological feel.

Tilly's House, St Edwards School, Oxford, OX2 7NN
Tel 01865 319257 Email jolleyp@stedwards.oxon.sch.uk

David Jones Fellow

The work focuses primarily on raku and a re-interpretation of the vessels associated with the Japanese tea ceremony. This interest has developed further into the ideas underpinning raku and other firing strategies with the publication of *Raku – Investigations into Fire* (1999) and the forthcoming book, *The Philosophy and Practice of Firings*. He teaches on the degree courses in the Ceramics department of Wolverhampton University; he has lectured, given workshops and exhibited extensively in this country and abroad.

21 Plymouth Place, Leamington Spa, Warwickshire, CV31 1HN Tel/Fax 01926 314643
Email davidjonesraku@lineone.net Website www.davidjonesceramics.co.uk or
www.fixinglight-fixingfire.co.uk Visitors welcome by appointment

Vresh David Kanikanian

I was born in Mosul, Iraq into an Armenian family. I graduated in 1957 from the Arts Institute, Baghdad. In 1960 I went to Chelsea School of Art and graduated in 1964, obtaining a NDD (National Diploma in Design) with painting as my specialist subject. My main work is functional and sculptural pieces based on thrown pots. I also demonstrated throwing double-walled pots, with Arabic calligraphy as cut-out designs on the outer wall, for many years at *Art in Action* in Waterperry near Wheatley, Oxfordshire. I joined Ealing School of Art in 1964, which subsequently became Thames Valley University, teaching ceramics. I have work in several collections: the Museum of Modern Art in Amman, Jordan; in Baghdad, Iraq and in the Veheran Holy Etchmiadzin, Armenia, and since 1989 my works are on permanent display at Gallery Tavid, Ealing, London.

Gallery Tavid, 56 St Mary's Road, Ealing, London, W5 5EX Tel 020 8566 1494
Gallery hours: Weekdays 2-9pm; Sat-Sun 11am-9pm; or by appointment

Lisa Katzenstein

My present work has been dedicated to reviving the status of 'floral' decoration in ceramics. However, it is floral with a modern twist, with an emphasis on wild plants. Once seen as weeds, these are now in our ecologically conscious times viewed as a marker for our changing relationship with the land and our sense of 'natural beauty'. All my work is white earthenware with tin glaze or maiolica hand-painted decoration. This technique, in which you paint on top of the glaze prior to firing, has a long history in European ceramics. I view my pots as paintings which also happen to be functional vases. My range includes vases, bowls and wall pieces and I use a variety of techniques such as wax resist and sgraffito.

Lisa Katzenstein '05

67 Tyrwhitt Road London, SE4 1QE Tel/Fax 020 8694 2428
Website www.lisakatzenstein.co.uk Visitors welcome by appointment

Walter Keeler Fellow

Trained at Harrow School of Art before the
Studio Pottery Course was established. First
studio 1965, present studio since 1976.
Maker of functional pottery of an individual
nature in saltglazed stoneware, some in
earthenware.

Moorcroft Cottage, Penallt, Monmouth, Gwent, NP25 4AH
Tel 01600 713946 Fax 01600 712530 Visitors welcome by appointment

Chris Keenan Fellow

The pots that I make are to be used and enjoyed in domestic life. There are certain forms that have been present in my work almost since I began making – cups, bowls, pots for flowers – and I still derive pleasure and satisfaction from the formal refinements that accompany each fresh exploration. I think that for me, the bowl remains the form where subtleties of line are most elusive and consequently most rewarding when successful. The work is thrown Limoges porcelain, gas fired using combinations of celadon and temmoku.

31 Balin House, Long Lane, London, SE1 1YQ Tel 020 7701 2940 Fax 020 7403 1067
Email powellkeenan@compuserve.com Website www.chriskeenan.com

Christy Keeney

After graduating from the Royal College of Art
in 1987 Christy worked in various studios in
London for seventeen years. In 2001 he
moved back to Ireland where he now works in
his studio, high in the Donegal mountains.
'The clay I use is a mixture of flax clay and St
Thomas, fired to 1140°C, painted with oxides
and underglaze colours. My work is constantly
evolving, and each piece teaches me a bit
more about what I am searching for.'

C. KEENEY   05

Doon Glebe, Newmills, Letterkenny, County Donegal, Ireland
Tel +353 (0)74 9167258 Email christykeeney@eircom.net

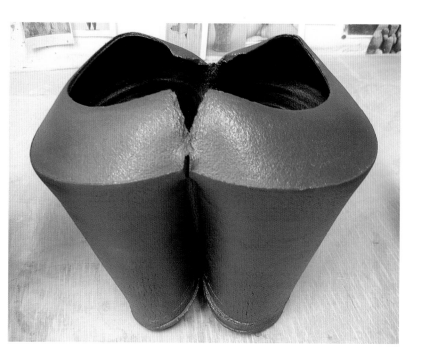

Dan Kelly

Trained at Camberwell School of Art and
Crafts and at the Royal College of Art in the
late 1970s, Dan Kelly lives and works in
London making individual pieces in
stoneware and porcelain. He also produces a
utilitarian range of oven to tableware. Dan
has exhibited widely both at home and
abroad taking part in both individual and
group shows.

Home: 15 Bicknell Road, London, SE5 9AU
Workshop: Clockwork Studios, 38A Southwell Road, London, SE5 9PG Tel 020 7733 1040

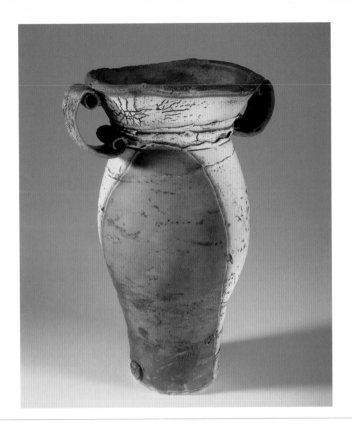

John Kershaw

I set up my workshop and showroom in
Windermere village in 1972. For many years
I produced a range of functional work: bread
crocks, storage jars and planters, fired in
electric kilns. I now concentrate on more
individual pieces, liking to work freely with
thrown forms, using the effects of powdered
ball clays on the wet thrown form to get
heavily encrusted surfaces. I have a taste for
ancient and primitive pottery, liking the
freedom and simple means of production,
and I like to get something of that quality
into my vessels.

40 Main Road, Windermere, Cumbria, LA23 1DY Tel 01539 444844
Email john@kershawpottery.com Website www.kershawpottery.com

Hyejeong Kim

I create stoneware ceramics, both domestic and sculptural work. I intend to create contemporary ceramic artwork based upon my own cultural tradition and style, to promote the aesthetic and artistic quality that such traditions produce. The tableware I make is simple with close attention to design and functionality. Shapes are formed on a wheel, but occasionally handbuilding or coiling techniques are combined. The majority of techniques and glazes that I have developed are derived from Chinese, Korean and Japanese traditional pottery. Using traditional Korean and Japanese pottery tools (for instance, stamps, wood sticks etc.), but also making use of natural instruments such as stones, shells, seeds, leaves, woods, etc. for decoration and to create texture on the clay surface. Firing cone 9 to 10 either in reduction or oxidisation atmosphere to get various glaze finishes.

Studio 8A, Iliffe Yard, Crampton Street, London, SE17 3QA
Tel 07929 152128 Email hyejeong@nifty.com Website www.potspots.co.uk

Ruth King Fellow

Trained at Camberwell School of Art and Craft from 1974-7 and established her own workshop in London in 1978. In 1981 she moved to York where she now lives and has her own studio. Her pots are handbuilt using varying techniques of construction to produce individual pieces in salt-glazed stoneware. Ruth King has exhibited throughout the UK and has work in collections at the Victoria and Albert Museum, London;

Castle Museum, Nottingham; Ulster Museum, Belfast; City Art Gallery, York; and the Museum of Scotland, Edinburgh.

Rose Cottage, Main Street, Shipton-by-Beningbrough, York, YO30 1AB Tel 01904 470196
Email ruth@ruthkingceramics.com Website www.ruthkingceramics.com Visitors welcome by appointment

Gabriele Koch Fellow

Her handbuilt, burnished and smoke-fired
vessel forms have been internationally
recognised for many years. Her work is
housed in many important public and private collections in the UK and abroad,
including the Victoria and Albert Museum,
the Sainsbury Collection, the Ashmolean
Museum in Oxford, and museums in
Frankfurt, Karlsruhe and Zurich. She
exhibits her work regularly in the UK,

Europe, the Middle East and America, and
every November in her own gallery, Studio
147 in London. A monograph has been published by Marston House Books.

Studio 147, 147 Archway Road, Highgate, London, N6 5BL Tel/Fax 020 8292 3169
Email gabrielekoch@blueyonder.co.uk Visitors welcome by appointment

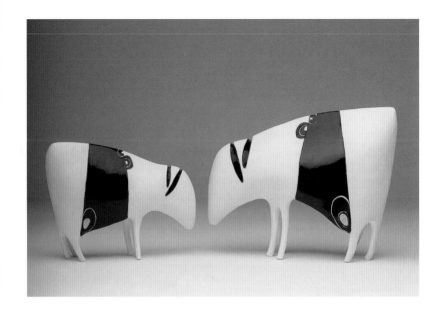

Daiva Kojelyte-Marrow

I trained at Vilnius Art Academy in Lithuania
and moved to Britain in 1998. My work con-
sists of individual handbuilt low-fired pieces,
decorated using slip, nichrome wire and
glazes. I like figurative and abstract forms
with a clear elegant shape. My work has been
exhibited in the UK and abroad, including
Museo Internazionale delle Ceramiche in
Faenza, Italy; Lithuanian Ceramics Museum
and Yingho Ceramics Museum, Taipei, Taiwan.

58 Queensgate, Northwich, Cheshire, CW8 1DU
Tel 01606 783619 Email james.marrow@manchester.ac.uk

Anna Lambert Fellow

I set up as a studio potter in Gloucestershire after graduating from Bath Academy of Art in 1980. In 1989 I relocated to Yorkshire and now share a studio with my husband in Crosshills, North Yorkshire. I make handbuilt earthenware. Each piece is constructed individually by pinching, coiling, modelling and relief decoration. After firing to 1085°C it is inlaid with black glaze and coloured with underglaze washes, oxides and transparent glazes. In making these pieces I am attempting to create a synthesis between my response to landscape and my delight in European decorative ceramics and folk art. Simple bowls to complex multiple forms have elements in common: interpretations of my rural surroundings, beautiful curves of hillsides, seashells found on a strand, birds glimpsed on a walk, cloud shadows, tractor lines. All these are set within the essential, functional nature of each piece.

Junction Workshop, 1 Skipton Road, Crosshills, North Yorkshire, BD20 7SB Tel 01535 631341
Email junction.works@virgin.net Visitors welcome by appointment

Nigel Lambert Fellow

Makes pots that are firmly rooted in the domestic tradition. Trained in Cornwall and North Devon, he has made his home in the Forest of Dean for the last fifteen years. The pots are a combination of thrown and hand-built elements. Nigel's current pots are ovaled and squared. These forms offer him many more surfaces onto which he expresses ideas with paintbrushes and anything else that comes to hand in the studio.

Decoration explores the relationship between man-made structures and the natural landscape. Buff earthenware clay is slipped and raw glazed; cobalt, iron and copper oxides are used for painting. More recent pots are fired a third time with an application of iron red enamels.

Golden Valley Cottage, Morse Lane, Drybrook, Gloucestershire, GL17 9BA Tel 01597 542251
Email nigel@nigellambertpotter.co.uk Website www.nigellambertpotter.co.uk

Jean-Paul Landreau

Born in the Loire Valley in France. I first trained as a dental technician. After moving to London in 1979 I studied ceramics at Harrow School of Art. I also worked and taught as a ceramic technician before setting up in rural Wales. In my work I use the surface like the painter uses a canvas, on which I paint multiple layers of coloured slips and sgraffito the motif. For more abstract motifs, I like the interplay of the motif to sing out to the viewer's own imagination. I have collaborated with John Piper, Bruce McLean, Philip Sutton and Patrick Caulfield. Exhibitions in the UK, France, USA and Holland.

Cross House, Tregaron, Ceredigion, SY25 6ND Tel 01974 298828
Email ceramics@jeanpaullandreau.fsnet.co.uk Website www.jean-paul-landreau.co.uk

The Ceramics Book | 161

Peter Lane Honorary Fellow

Author of *Studio Porcelain* (Pitman, 1980), *Studio Ceramics* (Collins, 1983), *Ceramic Form*, (Collins, 1988 and enlarged edition A&C Black, 1998), *Contemporary Porcelain*, (A&C Black, 1995) and *Contemporary Studio Porcelain* (A&C Black, 2003). Widely exhibited, he has given numerous lectures and demonstrations in Europe, Australia, New Zealand, Canada and USA. He makes mainly vessel forms in porcelain using designs inspired by landscape and natural phenomena with either carved, incised or atmospherically painted surfaces. Represented in many public and private collections including the City Museum and Art Gallery, Stoke-on-Trent; City of Aberdeen Museum and Art Gallery; Castle Museum, Norwich; The Royal Scottish Museum, Edinburgh; The National Gallery of Victoria, Melbourne, Australia; Utah Museum of Fine Arts, Salt Lake City, USA; etc.

Ivy House, 44 Jacklyns Lane, New Alresford, Hampshire, SO24 9LG
Tel 01962 735041 Email peter@studio-porcelain.co.uk Website www.studio-porcelain.co.uk

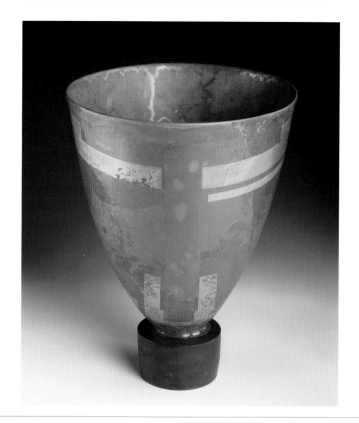

Tony Laverick

Tony Laverick trained at Preston Polytechnic from 1981-4. Full-time professional potter since 1988. My work is mostly thrown porcelain (1270°C) decorated with precious metal lustres.

Ridgeway House, Leek Road, Longsdon, Staffordshire, ST9 9QF Tel 01538 386050
Email tonylaverick@btinternet.com Website www.churnetcontemporaryarts.co.uk Visitors welcome by appointment

The Ceramics Book | 163

Liz Lawrence

Born on the south coast in 1951 and originally trained in graphic design at Worthing
Art College. Moved to Bristol in 1960, completed a BA (Hons) degree in ceramics at
University of the West of England in 2000.
Recently set up a workshop in south Wales.
Currently makes thrown, slip-decorated,
porcelain vessels. The work is instinctive and
inspiration is found from many aspects of
the visual world. The designs are achieved
by resist or sgraffito pattern making techniques and the work is raw-fired to stoneware
temperatures in an oxidised electric kiln.

40 The Nurseries, Langstone, Newport, Monmouthshire, NP18 2NT Tel 01633 411417 Mobile 07977 055563
Email liz_lawrence@lineone.net Website www.southwalespotters.org.uk Visitors welcome by appointment

Wendy Lawrence

I have an obsession with texture, particularly in rocks and geological structure, which I document on walks in north Wales and travels further afield. Using this information I make ceramic pieces which at some times are spontaneous and at others carefully carved, attempting to capture the energy and power of geological form and describe the ordered structure of rock strata. Glazing is unconventional, using highly reactive and eruptive materials applied in multiple layers, often very thickly, creating rich textural surfaces. This process of glazing furthers the sense of geological quality and provides an element of chance. I fire the pieces to around 1260°C in gas and electric kilns, varying the kiln atmosphere from oxidation to heavy reduction.

Ty Tal, 34 Park Street, Denbigh, Denbighshire, North Wales, LL16 3DB Tel 01745 814441
Email wlawrenceceramics@hotmail.com Website www.wendylawrenceceramics.com Visitors welcome by appointment

John Leach Fellow

John Leach continues the family tradition, hand throwing and wood firing domestic and individual pots at Muchelney, the pottery he set up in 1965 near Langport in Somerset. He works with a small team – his wife Lizzie and master potters Nick Rees and Mark Melbourne. The pottery is idyllically situated on the Somerset Levels one mile south of the ancient village of Muchelney, famed for its 10th century abbey. The pottery is open all year, with workshop viewing by appointment and on advertised public kiln opening days. Visitors may also walk around John's conservation pond, a country wildlife site and explore the nearby delights of cider and brandy making, traditional fish smoking and willow basket making.

Roger Lewis

Born 1946. Trained at Shrewsbury, High Wycombe, Cardiff and Goldsmiths. Senior lecturer of ceramics for over twenty years up to 1997. My main working method has evolved over thirty years of continuous development exploring the possibilities derived by inventive manipulation of thin slabs of clay. Ideas for forms come from this exploration of the material. I try to develop interesting and sometimes unusual ways of making objects out of clay and then spend a period of time exploring the possibilities. My search with clay can lead me to spin off in new directions unexpectedly. The work is balanced between the initial excitement and motivation gained from experimental discovery and the subsequent satisfaction of perfecting and developing ideas through limited production.

6 Chellow Terrace, Bradford, West Yorkshire, BD9 6AY Tel 01274 495380 Email rogerlewis@theceramicartist.com
Website www.theceramicartist.com Visitors welcome by appointment

Barbara Lock

Pots are handbuilt, often starting with a thumb pot, then building from that base. Stained shafts of clay are woven into the pots once they have been formed. After being smoothed over and oxides rubbed in, the pots are painted with many thin washes of coloured slips that bleed into each other. Sometimes areas are masked off for more dramatic effect. After prolonged burnishing, the pots are dried out thoroughly and then elec-tric-fired, usually once. Her concerns are to do with: contrasts; exploration of cause and effect; risk taking; use of space, form and line; the building up of layers and the influence each has on the other; use of colour and the never-ending changes and subtleties therein. These concerns find their expression in shadows, contours, pebbles, rocks, water, movement. The Pembrokeshire coast and the Welsh mountains are a particular reference.

UK: 44 Beatty Avenue, Cardiff, CF23 5QU Tel 029 2075 5863 Email barbara@pottery.fsnet.co.uk
France: Le Bez, Vabre Tizac, 12240 France
Websites www.southwalespotters.org.uk www.makersguildinwales.org.uk www.artmatters.org.uk

Susan Luker

The colours and contours of south Devon's coast and country inspire Susan Luker's unique sculptural ceramics. Influenced by Brancusi, Moore and Hepworth, Susan uses abstraction to convey powerfully and directly and share her love and feelings for the beautiful and moving landscape in which she lives and works. Each smoke-fired raku work is individually handbuilt and lovingly burnished. Striking rivers of copper or green glaze flow across the burnished surface, evoking the setting sun shimmering on river and marsh. Susan exhibits widely across the country and her work has been on show at the Victoria and Albert Museum. She is a member of the Devon Guild of Craftsmen.

Susan Luker.

**The Workshop, Hatch Court, Loddiswell, Kingsbridge, Devon, TQ7 4AJ Mobile 07779 923502
Email susanluker@raku.fsbusiness.co.uk Visitors and school residencies by appointment**

Martin Lungley

I produce a range of thrown porcelain
tableware and larger, more individual
pieces. Larger individual pieces explore
material qualities and the narrative of
process. Fluidity, movement and softness
are qualities I aim to explore in all my
work.

14 Tribune Drive, Houghton, Carlisle, Cumbria, CA3 0LE
Mobile 07811 038116 Email martinlungley@yahoo.com Visitors welcome by appointment

The Ceramics Book | 170

Sophie MacCarthy

Sophie MacCarthy has lived and worked in the East End of London for over twenty years, during which time she has developed a distinctive and personal ceramic style. She is an accomplished thrower and has a sensitive eye for form, producing classically elegant pieces such as tall jugs, large open bowls, plates and teapots. With her bold use of coloured slips, painterly brushwork, wax resist and stencils, she has explored themes such as landscape (urban as well as rural), nature, rhythm and movement to great effect. Sells through Contemporary Ceramics, London; The Scottish Gallery, Edinburgh; Charleston Farmhouse, Sussex.

Alasdair Neil MacDonell

I make a wide range of sculptural forms, mostly wall-hanging, that use textures and patterns derived from found objects, wrappings and industrial scrap. Faces are a central theme but the work also reflects my interest in architecture, antiquities and tribal art. All pieces are unique.

ANM
BATH

2 Kennington Road, Bath, BA1 3EA Tel 01225 465996 Email neil@macdonell-ceramics.co.uk
Website www.macdonell-ceramics.co.uk Visitors welcome by appointment

Sally MacDonell

Sally MacDonell models figures with slabs of stoneware clay, forming tubes from which the work evolves. Oxides and engobes are washed on before firing to 1170°C. The work is then finished with a sawdust firing which creates the distinctive, subtle patterns of smoke. She lives and works in Bath with her husband Alasdair MacDonnell.

Sally MacDonell
Bath

2 Kennington Road, Bath, BA1 3EA Tel 01225 465996 Email sally@macdonell-ceramics.co.uk
Website www.macdonell-ceramics.co.uk Visitors welcome by appointment

Jane Maddison

Recently my work has assumed a totally different scale and direction. I now produce small and affordable domestic ware using animal themes on porcelain, often with sgraffito design etched through background colour. I sell through many shops and galleries throughout the UK and Ireland.

The Old School Cottages, Stragglethorpe, Lincoln, LN5 0QZ
Tel 01400 272971 Email jkmaddison@aol.com

Made in Cley

Made in Cley is a craft co-operative established in 1981 comprising seven potters and a jeweller: Wolf Altmann, Gunhild Espelage, Christiane Guenther, Richard Kelham, Mary Perry, Rosalind Redfern, Barbara Widdup and Quay Proctor-Mears (jeweller). We produce a wide range of wheel-thrown reduction and oxidised fired stoneware for domestic use. In addition to our domestic range we make individual sculptural pieces in stoneware for the house and garden. Commissions undertaken. We sell our work in our own gallery where we also have our workshops.

Made in Cley, High Street, Cley-next-the-Sea, Nr Holt, Norfolk, NR25 7RF Tel 01263 740134
Fax 01263 740186 Email madeincley@aol.com Website www.madeincley.co.uk
The gallery is open all year, Mon-Sat 10am-5pm, Sun 11am-4pm

Fenella Mallalieu Fellow

My main interest in ceramics lies in form and colour; to combine generous expansive forms with rich organic colours. After twenty years of being a potter, I still love throwing – I love the immediacy of the process and the fluidity of the material when wet. I enjoy making wide bowls of all sizes and fat-bellied shapes such as jugs and teapots. The bowls are distorted with two or three folds in the rim, made when the clay is still very soft. Over the years my palette of glazes has expanded from three or four very simple ones originating from the Tang period to about ten colours, all derived from different combinations of just two oxides.

100 Mortimer Road, London, N1 4LA Tel 020 7241 6553
Fax 020 7249 5341 Visitors welcome by appointment

Jim Malone Fellow

'There may be people who prefer to deal with the problems of modernity – its alienation, its disruption, its ever-increasing speed, automation and impersonalisation – by embracing what they see as the "real" contemporary: industrial manufacture and a "modern" aesthetic. But equally there are thousands who like to have, hold and use things equally well designed, actually equally "modern" in aesthetic terms, but that are demonstrably handmade, the product of an individual working with a simpler technology. For them, these things are more expressive, have richer meanings and longer resonances. This is the space in which potters like Jim Malone work.' (Oliver Watson, Victoria and Albert Museum, Feb 1997)

Dairy Lea Cottage, Lessonhall, Wigton, Cumbria, CA7 0EA
Tel 01697 345241 Visitors welcome

West Marshall Fellow

West Marshall studied pottery on the Harrow Studio Pottery course (now the University of Westminster) where from 1976 until 2002 he taught on the BA (Hons) Ceramics course. Since 1970 he has been making thrown domestic ware. He is currently using Southern Ice porcelain body because of its stunning whiteness and beautiful translucency. His present fascination is with crisply thrown tableware. Forms are simple and uncluttered.

Decoration is achieved through the minimal use of clean, delicate, incised lines.

118 White Hill, Chesham, Buckinghamshire, HP5 1AR Tel 01494 785969 Email west.marshall@ntlworld.com
Website www.westmarshall.co.uk Small showroom open to visitors by appointment

Will Levi Marshall Fellow

BA Hons 3D Design Manchester Metropolitan University. MFA (Ceramics) Alfred University, USA. Currently running a studio in south-west Scotland, exhibiting and lecturing internationally. I have a background in thrown tableware, however my current focus is on architectural installations. These are often tile/block based although my repertoire of materials includes glass, concrete, stainless steel, stone and water. I aim to produce integrated,

durable site-specific artworks that create cerebral and visual dynamics within a space without compromising its fundamental function. The commissioning process includes consultation, 3D designs, manufacture, management of subcontracts and installation. I work with public and private clients on interior and exterior projects and am happy to accept commissions. I also produce a range of hand-thrown and glazed presentation dishes.

Holm Studio, Auchencairn, Castle Douglas, Dumfries and Galloway, DG7 1QL Tel 01556 640399
Fax 01556 640116 Mobile 07790 718783 Email will.marshall@btopenworld.com
Visitors welcome by appointment

Andrew Mason

I was born and raised in a traditional, non-artistic family in close proximity to the pottery industry in north Staffordshire. I was captivated by pottery lessons at school and attracted towards the kiln shed where 'smoking' was about inhaling nicotine rather than doing something to pots. A modest talent for art and a strong interest in an alternative lifestyle led me to art school. This social and educational paradox has fostered a diverse outlook and a strong historical and cultural interest. I have run my own studio since 1986, gaining much valuable practical, and associated professional, experience. Most of my work is thrown: I love the rhythmic sensation of throwing, though remain open to further exploring other areas and techniques of ceramics. I like to use rich, colourful glazes and still get a thrill from pressing the button on my electric kiln controller.

3 Stiles Road, Alvaston, Derby, DE24 0PG
Tel 01332 753799 Email andymasonceramics@btinternet.com

Gareth Mason

The 'corporeal' allure of clay is largely unsung in ceramics discourse, which is a shame because making involves a special kind of close-to-the-body physicality, the mysteries of which merit deeper unravelling than merely 'how it is done'. Pots, at their best, entice the viewer to touch, often furtively. Detached intellect is rarely the root of this tactile encounter; the call is altogether earthier. Clay is in fact a deeply sexy medium and this underpins my continual attraction to the wheel, which is – almost worryingly – sensual in nature. Throwing stirs my blood. I make pots in a spirit of perpetual anticipation, like seduction, like life. Not surprisingly, this can be an intense experience. It is quite a trip. (Photo: Abbas Nazari)

7 Old Acre Road, Alton, Hampshire, GU34 1NR Tel 01420 543573
Email gi.mason@virgin.net Visitors welcome by appointment

May Ling Mason Fellow

May Ling Mason trained at the University of
Derby and in the workshops of Josie Walter,
John Wheeldon and John Leach. She established her first studio in 1996 with husband
Andy Mason. 'I love the tactile experience of
working with clay – the coolness and pliabil-
ity of plastic clay and the contrasting
warmth and permanence of fired work fresh
from the kiln.'

3 Stiles Road, Alvaston, Derby, DE24 0PG
Tel 01332 753799 Email maylingceramics@btinternet.com

John Mathieson

I started making pots at evening class in
London, began teaching pottery at secondary level one year later and have since taken
a degree in ceramics. I now make individual
pieces in stoneware and raku on a slow
wheel. The stoneware is reduction-fired to
cone 10 in a gas kiln using a variety of slips
and glazes. I am the author of *Raku*, published by A&C Black as part of its Ceramics
Handbooks series.

50 Ridgeway, Weston Favell, Northampton, NN3 3AN Tel 01604 409942 Email mathieson@ic24.net
Website www.studiopottery.co.uk or www.theceramicartist.com Visitors welcome by appointment

Marcio Mattos Fellow

Individual stoneware and paperclay vessels, with reduction-fired, sprayed and brushed glazes emphasising surface texture. Handbuilt sculptural vases, teapots, jugs, plates and bowls. Trained initially in music, later took a post-graduate degree in ceramics at Goldsmiths College. Has exhibited and given lectures/demonstrations both in Britain and abroad, with works in private and public collections in Holland, France, Germany, Japan, Brazil and New Zealand. As in music, the immediacy and spontaneity of improvisation is important to his work.

7 Broadway Market Mews, Hackney, London, E8 4TS Tel 020 7254 1351 Fax 020 7503 8417
Email marcio@musiclay.freeserve.co.uk Website www.musiclay.freeserve.co.uk Visitors welcome by appointment

Christine McCole

Trained at Harrow on the studio pottery
course, 1977-9. Moved to Wales with her partner, Roger Brann, and converted the smithy at
Llanboidy to set up the workshop in 1980.
They produce a wide range of domestic
stoneware glazed in buff, green and temmoku,
and a small quantity of garden stoneware. The
pots are wood-fired over twelve hours to
1280°C, in a 40 cu.ft fast-fire kiln based on
Doug Phillips's version of Fred Olsen's design.

LLANBOIDY

Hafod Hill Pottery, Llanboidy, Whitland, Carmarthenshire, SA34 OER Tel 01994 448361
Email potters@hafodhillpottery.com Website www.hafodhillpottery.com Visitors welcome

Laurence McGowan Fellow

Born Salisbury 1942. Set up own workshop in 1979 after earlier career making maps and interpreting aerial photos in various parts of the world. Trained at Alvingham and with Alan Caiger-Smith, Aldermaston. Traditional majolica decorative techniques are employed on quiet, wheel-thrown functional forms. Various stain and oxide mixtures are painted on zirconium opacified Cornish Stone based glazes, electric-fired to cone 8 (1260°C). Decorative motifs are taken from plant and animal forms, applied to both enhance the pot's form and reflect something of the exuberance of nature. Interests relating to the work include lettering/calligraphy and the decorative arts of the Islamic world.

6 Aughton, Collingbourne Kingston, Marlborough, Wiltshire, SN8 3SA Tel 01264 850749
Email pottery@mcgowan.charitydays.co.uk Website www.laurencemcgowan.co.uk Visitors welcome by appointment

Lesley McShea

I studied a Diploma (Honours) at Caufield Institute of Technology in Melbourne, Australia, where I gained a thorough knowledge of glazes, then completed a BA Honours degree in Ceramics at Middlesex University in 1992. Since then I have been producing one-off elevated stemmed vessels, birdbaths and sconces. My work is mostly wheel-thrown/press-moulded combinations, using a mixture of craft crank and white stoneware. I teach adults in my studio as well as adult education.

Church Street Workshops, Guttridges Yard, 172 Stoke Newington Church Street, London, N16 0JL
Tel 020 7241 3676 Website www.geocities.com/lesleymcs

Martin McWilliam Fellow

What I am looking for in my work with clay and fire lies in their own essential beauty and the play between them: a beauty subjective, difficult to define, control or repeat; something to do with chance coincidence. My methods are as simple/direct as possible where chance has space to surprise. This leads me along a narrow ridge between my will and that of the material. I make coil/slab-built stoneware *trompe-l'œil*

objects, coloured with kaolin slips, all wood-fired in a 6 cubic metre chamber kiln. They give the idea of simple bowls and jars, of a tradition that has given me a lifelong fascination, but take them into another space of the mind.

Auf dem Kötjen 1, D-26209 Sandhatten, Germany
Tel +49 (0) 4482 8372 Email ceramics@martin-mcwilliam.de Website www.martin-mcwilliam.de

Peter Meanley Fellow

Peter Meanley works with saltglaze and makes ranges of spouted pouring vessels and teapots. All vessels must pour and indeed the aspect of pouring is often an integral part of the pleasure of designing and thinking about the next idea to be made. Peter is an avid collector of objects, often domestic and sometimes historical which might have features to assist his thinking. His kiln, which is sited on a farm in the country, is fired approximately six times a year. He likes heavy orange peel and sometimes makes a particular feature of this. Until recently Peter was a reader at the University of Ulster where he completed a D Phil into saltglaze. His work is in a wide range of national and international collections and museums.

pm
o5

6 Downshire Road, Bangor, County Down, Northern Ireland, BT20 3TW Tel/Fax 028 9146 6831
Email teapots@meanley.freeserve.co.uk Visitors welcome by appointment

Eric James Mellon Honorary Fellow

Born 1925. Studied Watford, Harrow and Central School of Arts and Crafts, London. Creates brush-drawn decorated ceramic fired to 1300°C, using tree and bush ash glazes. Represented in the Victoria and Albert Museum and collections in Britain and internationally. 'Drawing on to clay is firing thoughts into ceramic. The concern is not academic correctness in drawing but to create work of visual decorative poetic surprise and aesthetic satisfaction.' See: Phil Rogers, *Ash Glazes* (A&C Black, 2003); Paul Foster, *Eric James Mellon – Ceramic Artist* (University College Chichester, 2000) and *Ceramic Review* No's. 42/43-1977, 65-1980, *Magic and Poetry* in 114-1988, 172-1998, 183-2000.

Eric James Mellon

5 Parkfield Avenue, Bognor Regis, West Sussex, PO21 3BW Tel 01243 268949
Visitors welcome by appointment

Kate Mellors

I trained at Camberwell School of Art 1972-5 and on leaving taught part-time in adult education and set up my pottery making tableware and decorative pieces. A long-standing interest in gardens, architecture and outdoor pottery inspired a new direction. In 1985 I began making pots for the garden, influences coming from south east Asia and Africa. I moved to rural west Dorset in 1990 and now work full-time making a range of garden lanterns, birdbaths, planters, stools and water features. The work is thrown, slabbed, press-moulded, glazed and once-fired in a gas kiln.

Mellors

Mellors Garden Ceramics, Rosemead, Marshwood, Bridport, Dorset, DT6 5QB Tel/Fax 01297 678217
Email kate@mellors-ceramics.co.uk Website www.mellors-ceramics.co.uk Visitors welcome by appointment

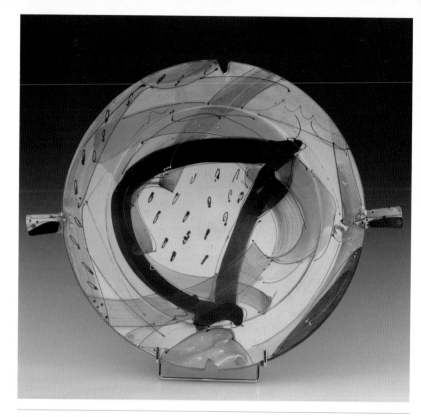

David Miller Fellow

Born in London. Studied sculpture, printmaking and ceramics at Ravensbourne and Brighton colleges of art, now living and working in southern France. Fifteen years ago established a workshop in Collorgues, a small village near Nimes. I make decorated slipware inspired by traditional French *terre vernissée*, comprising a range of functional ware and one-off pieces. Exhibited in France, Holland, Germany and England.

Rue du Ranc, 30190 Collorgues, France Tel/Fax +33 (0) 466 819119
Email ceramicdavidmiller@yahoo.fr Website www.ceramique.com/David-Miller

Sean Miller

Sean Miller set up his own workshop in
1991 after completing the BTEC HND course
at Harrow. He makes thrown and slipped
earthenware pottery for domestic use. The
decoration is inspired by traditional
European slipware. The range includes
bowls, baking dishes, jars, plates etc and is
both oven-proof and dishwasher safe.

108 Dewsbury Road, London, NW10 1EP Tel 020 8208 0148 Mobile 07792 202477
Email seanpots@btinternet.com Website www.theceramicartist.com

Toff Milway Fellow

I specialise in high temperature salt-glazed stoneware using pure clay slips. I have adapted some traditional slipware techniques to produce finely textured surfaces on a variety of domestic ware and individual dinner services. Recent work incorporates three-dimensional fish as handles on jugs and dishes. After extended periods abroad working in Africa and USA, I now live and work in the beautiful Cotswold village of Conderton where I sell all I make from my own studio. Commissions undertaken. Regular exhibitions.

Conderton Pottery, The Old Forge, Conderton, Nr Tewkesbury, Gloucestershire, GL20 7PP Tel/Fax 01386 725387
Website www.toffmilway.co.uk Workshop and showroom open Mon-Sat 9am-5pm; phone at other times.
Always a large selection of work on display

Ursula Mommens Honorary Fellow

I studied for three years at the Central School, then a stroke of luck made it possible to work at the Royal College of Art under William Staite Murray for two years. I started on my own, converting an old cowhouse in Kent, and later I had the great good fortune to work at Wenford Bridge with Michael Cardew, who has been my chief inspiration ever since. I set up my present pottery forty-five years ago with Norman Mommens, and continue to make use-ful stoneware using our own clay body and ash glazes, fired to 1300°C in Chris Lewis's big wood-fired kiln and my small gas one. I have exhibited widely: at the Bloomsbury Gallery, Primavera (as Ursula Darwin), Galerie Besson, Harlequin and St Matthews in London; Kettles Yard in Cambridge; Stonegate in York; St Ives; New Ashgate Farnham; Bettles in Ringwood and locally, in the Gardiner Centre and Towner Hastings and Hove Museums.

The Pottery, South Heighton, Newhaven, Sussex, BN9 0HL
Tel 01273 514408

Sarah Monk

I am a potter who specialises in breakfast ware, designed to start the day on a cheery note. For this reason I choose to work in white earthenware clay. Once fired, the whiteness of the bisque provides the perfect canvas for my bright 'sunshine' yellow glaze. Pretty much everything I make is functional. It gives me great pleasure when customers express their delight in regularly using my work. Inspiration is drawn in part from nature and from an interest in Victorian art pottery. My father collects antique china, so I grew up surrounded by weird and wonderful objects from history. An ornate ceramic wig stand from the Victorian era comes to mind. The decorative images drawn from nature are slightly stylised, often humorous, cartoon-like representations. My intention again, is to put a smile on the face of the user.

SARAH
MONK

Eastnor Pottery, Home Farm, Eastnor, Ledbury, Herefordshire, HR8 1RD Tel/Fax 01531 633886
Email eastnor.pottery@ukonline.co.uk Website www.eastnorpottery.co.uk Visitors welcome by appointment

Aki Moriuchi Fellow

Over the years, 'time' has become the most
important element to me. I try to capture
the essence of time in my work – something
which I can see in weathered stones. I was
born in Tokyo, Japan and studied ceramics
at Harrow College and Middlesex University.
I now live in Cornwall.

Home: 4 Menhyr Drive, Carbis Bay, St Ives, Cornwall TR26 2QR Tel 01736 793064
Studio: Gaolyard Studios, Dove Street, St Ives, Cornwall TR26 2LZ Visitors to the studio welcome by appointment
Email akimoriuchi@hotmail.com Website www.gaolyard-studio-pottery.co.uk

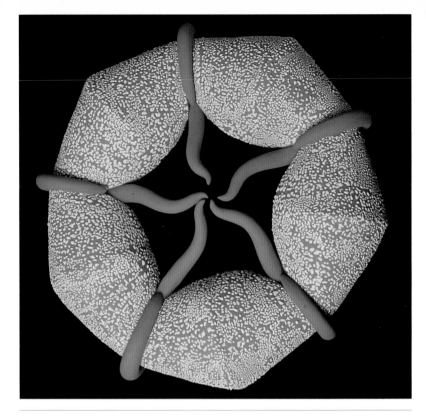

Catrin Mostyn Jones

Inspired by nature at a microscopic level, together with fragmented textures and colours of the deep sea. A vivid collection of handbuilt, press-moulded sculptural forms, brought to life by the addition of growths using coils and sculpted textures. I use a wide range of 960-1060°C earthenware glazes with a distinctive texture, which I spray in multiple layers, sometimes using a wax resist. This achieves an effect that has been described as a neon hallucination of a coral reef.

Drumcroon Gallery, 2 Parsons Walk, Wigan, WN1 1RS Mobile 07787 507228
Email vividceramics@hotmail.com Website www.vividceramics.co.uk

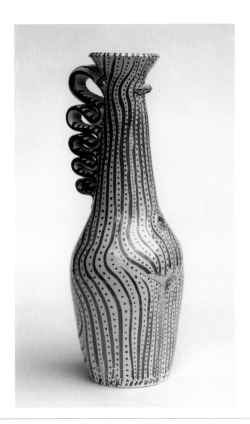

Roger Mulley

Ceramics both traditional and sculptural
using the human form and nature as inspiration. Current work includes large figurative
bowls and part-thrown sculpted figures.
Work is exhibited regularly and sold through
the pottery at Clanfield, south Hampshire,
established in 1976. Roger Mulley's ceramics
can be found in collections in both the UK
and abroad.

Clanfield Pottery, 131 Chalton Lane, Clanfield, Waterlooville, Hampshire, PO8 0RQ Tel 023 9259 5144
Fax 023 9235 1499 Email info@rogermulleyceramics.co.uk Website www.rogermulleyceramics.co.uk

Stephen Murfitt

Produces handbuilt and raku-fired ceramics.
His work has been exhibited widely at home
and abroad. Recent outlets have been
International Art Consultants, Bonhams and
the Hart Gallery in London. Author of the
recently published *The Glaze Book* (Thames &
Hudson). Stephen's pots are included in many
private, public and corporate collections.

SM

The Workshop, 18 Stretham Road, Wicken, Cambridgeshire, CB7 5XH
Tel 01353 721160 Visitors welcome by appointment

Claire Murray

My figurative ceramics are at present based around an exploration of the complexities of human communication. Speech does not always convey exactly what we might need or wish to say. Nor is it always received in the way that we might want. Communication may be through other ways such as the use of certain signs and symbols with which we might adorn our bodies. Some symbols could be considered as personal totems. All pieces are individually hand-modelled using Earthstone ST clay. They are fired to 1060°C initially and then finished with a mixture of manganese dioxide, red iron oxides plus a variety of underglaze colours and transparent earthenware glaze. The final firing is to 1100°C. Some pieces are sited on burnt oak bases, secured in place with a metal rod fixed with epoxy resin glue. The work is finished with a satin varnish.

The Old Coach House, Ashreigney, Chulmleigh, Devon, EX18 7NB Tel 01769 520775
Email clairemurray@btinternet.com Visitors welcome by appointment

Emily Myers Fellow

In 1990, three years after graduating from Bristol Polytechnic in ceramics, Emily Myers became a member of the Craft Potters Association, and the following year a Crafts Council Selected Maker. Exhibitions to date have included regular solo shows at Contemporary Ceramics in London and Beaux Arts in Bath. Emily throws strong elegant forms in red stoneware clay; once leather-hard, pots are often faceted or carved.

Barium glazes fired in an electric kiln result in striking, variegated matt glazes. Emily Myers lives and works in north Hampshire.

2 Chalkpit Cottages, Tangley, Andover, Hampshire, SP11 0RX Tel 01264 730243
Email emily@emilymyers.com Website www.emilymyers.com Visitors welcome by appointment

The Ceramics Book | 202

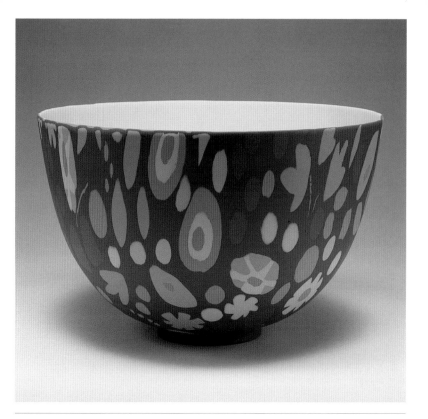

Susan Nemeth Fellow

I make porcelain bowls, vases and plates
inspired by fabric designs from the 1950s and
1960s. The decoration is integral. Laminated
sheets of coloured clays inlaid with hand cut
patterns are rolled, beaten and stretched over
moulds. The vases are slab-built. Buried in
sand to prevent warping, the pieces are highly
fired to achieve a smooth, matt, vitrified surface. They vary in size from 12-45cm. I exhibit my work in Britain, Europe and the USA.

Nemeth

Unit G6, The Chocolate Factory, Farleigh Place, Stoke Newington, London, N16 7SX Mobile 07855 002678
Email susan@snemeth.fsnet.co.uk Website www.hiddenart.com/susannemeth
Please email or phone for open studio details or an appointment

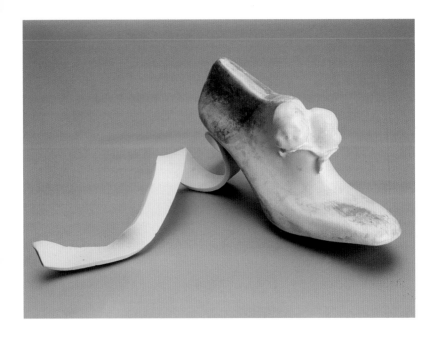

Christine Niblett

Christine Niblett works in stained millefiore porcelain, a layering technique in which the porcelain clay is coloured with natural metal oxides in its raw state and then assembled into patterned slabs from which the porcelain forms are press-moulded and handbuilt, before reduction gas firing to 1260°C. Although born in the UK, now living between London and Palma de Mallorca makes it easier to participate in events in Europe, the highlights of which, up to now, have been *Arte-Fiera* in Bologna, *OB'ART* in Paris and visits to Hungary to work with other ceramists in Siklós and Kecskemét.

Carrer Xesc Forteza 5, Valldemossa, 07170 Mallorca, Spain
Tel +34 (0) 971 616172 or 020 7824 8625 Fax +34 (0) 971 616098 Visitors welcome by appointment

Jeremy Nichols

I trained at the University of Westminster, graduating in 1997 and now divide my time between making at my Hertfordshire studio and teaching ceramics in adult education. I combine throwing and slipcasting to make saltglazed pots, mainly teapots and pouring vessels of one kind or another, along with cups and mugs of varying shapes and sizes. My original training as an aeronautical engineer is a major influence on both my methods of making the pots and in the sense of physical and visual balance I aim to achieve in their design.

32A Sellons Avenue, London, NW10 4HH Tel 020 8961 0409 Email jeremy@nichols70.freeserve.co.uk
Visitors to my Broxbourne, Hertfordshire, studio are welcome. Please contact me for directions.

Marcus O'Mahony

Born London 1952. In 1993 I established Glencairn Pottery near Lismore, County Waterford, Ireland, where I make saltglaze and wood-fired pottery. The pots I make are wheel-thrown and largely functional. I attempt to make pots that have an enduring quality, unconcerned with fashion or trends but which express my love of the ceramic process. When throwing with soft clay I try to create a sense of immediacy, movement and freshness in the forms. The pots are then often treated by altering the forms; faceting, stamping and drawing into the wet clay. They are decorated with slips, celadon and shino glazes and fired to 1300°C in the salt kiln and two or three times a year in the naborigama-style wood-fired kiln. I also run courses here at my studio.

Glencairn Pottery, Lismore, County Waterford, Ireland Tel +353 (0) 58 56694 Email info@marcusomahony.com
Website www.marcusomahony.com Visitors welcome to the workshop and small gallery by appointment

The Ceramics Book | 206

Jitka Palmer

Born in Prague, where I studied medicine and worked as an anatomist. In 1985 I moved to Britain. In 1987 I graduated from Croydon College of Art and Design and set up my first studio in London with the help of a Crafts Council Setting Up Grant. My work is figurative, narrative and expressive. My vessels are inspired by stories and themes. I draw on personal experiences, past and present with a view to reflect the spon- taneity of ordinary human life. I make large handbuilt clay vessels, painted with coloured slips, oxides and stains. I am trying to create tension between the outside and inside surface in order to give the whole piece another dimension. I have exhibited in Britain, Europe and USA. My work is in pri- vate and public collections including Musée National de Ceramique, Paris. I like working to commission.

Jitka Palmer

3 Florence Park, Westbury Park, Bristol, BS6 7LS Tel 0117 924 3473
Email jitka.palmer@bigfoot.com Website www.jitkapalmer.co.uk Visitors welcome by appointment

Sue Paraskeva

I work on a stick-driven momentum wheel and produce a simple range of tableware in a mixed porcelain body. Bowls are altered after turning to create movement. Work is glazed inside, polished outside, and both reduction and oxidation firings are used to create a speckled pale grey and cream ware. I have always been interested in using ceramics in different ways, hanging pots to fill large window displays. In 2004 I was commissioned to create a public art piece for the terrace wall at Quay Arts Centre, Newport, Isle of Wight – a sunburst created out of ninety porcelain panels. I also throw fine cylindrical forms in porcelain with intuitive decorative marks ranging from 10-40cm diameter – as wide as my kiln.
(Photo of work: Sue Paraskeva. Portrait: Steve Collins)

Studio One, Jubilee Stores, The Quay, Newport, Isle of Wight, PO30 2EF Tel 01983 522399
Email sue@paraskevapots.com Website www.sueparaskeva.co.uk Visitors welcome by appointment

Stephen Parry

Wood-fired stoneware and porcelain. Parry
trained at Croydon College of Art 1974-7,
Dartington Pottery Workshop 1977-9 and in
France using wood-fired kilns. Set up present pottery in Norfolk in 1981, making a
range of domestic ware and one-off pots
using both stoneware and porcelain clays.
Glazes are made from different types of
wood ash. Pots are fired in a 120 cubic foot
crossdraught wood-fired kiln, to 1300°C.

Ryburgh Pottery, Little Ryburgh, Fakenham, Norfolk, NR21 0LP Tel 01328 829543
Email steve@ryburghpottery.fsnet.co.uk Showroom at the pottery

Jane Perryman Fellow

Jane Perryman trained at Hornsey College of Art and later spent a year at the Keramisch Werkcentrum in Holland. Her work is concerned with an exploration of the vessel form using the traditional making and firing techniques of India and Africa with a contemporary interpretation. She exhibits worldwide and her work appears in a number of museums and private collections as well as being featured in many books and publi-

cations. She combines studio work with writing; her books include *Smoke-fired Pottery* (A&C Black, 1995), *Traditional Pottery of India* (A&C Black, 2000) and *Naked Clay* (A&C Black, 2004). A new edition of *Smoke-fired Pottery* will be published in 2007. She also runs workshops from her studio each summer and gives lectures and workshops in Europe and the USA.

Wash Cottage, Clare Road, Hundon, Suffolk, CO10 8DH Tel 01440 786228
Email janeperryman@btinternet.com Website www.janeperryman.com Visitors welcome by appointment

Richard Phethean Fellow

Studied at Camberwell School of Art and in the studios of Colin Pearson and Janice Tchalenko, 1972-8. I currently make dishes, bowls and sculptural vessel forms using coarse terracotta which are thrown, altered and reassembled, with slab additions. Surfaces are brushed with coloured and vitreous slips, used with resist, sgraffito and clear earthenware glazes. I make domestic slipware to commission only. I teach throw-ing on the ceramics degree course at the University of Westminster, Harrow, and offer intensive throwing blocks in my studio at Sibford School, where I live and work as resident potter. Author of *The Complete Potter: Throwing* (Batsford, 1991) with *An Introduction to Throwing,* a companion video cassette, and *The Complete Practical Potter* throwing chapter (Lorenz, 1999).

2 Hillfield, Sibford Ferris, Banbury, Oxfordshire, OX15 5QS Tel 01295 780041
Email phethean@clara.co.uk Website www.phethean.clara.net Visitors welcome by appointment

John Pollex Fellow

John Pollex worked as technician at Harrow College of Art (1968-70) after which he became assistant to Bryan Newman and then Colin Pearson. He moved to Plymouth in 1971 and established a reputation making traditional slipware. In the mid 1980s he felt the need for a change. He now produces highly individual pieces, richly painted with vibrant coloured slips using sponges, brushes and spatulas. The images are usually abstract and often reflect his interest in Eastern meditative philosophies and art. He particularly enjoys the personal contact to be found in lectures/demonstrations and has featured in over fifty workshops given in the UK and overseas.

Stowford House, 43 Seymour Avenue, St Judes, Plymouth, Devon, PL4 8RB Tel 01752 224902
Email john@johnpollex.co.uk Website www.johnpollex.co.uk

Philomena Pretsell

Bright domestic vessels with playful surface
imagery often reflecting contemporary
trends and high street influences.
Distinctive teapots, jugs, mugs, vases and
dishes combine handbuilding and various
print techniques to produce colourful and
often humorous pots. Work is held in private
and public collections in Europe and abroad.

P. M. P.

Rose Cottage, 10 Fountain Place, Loanhead, Midlothian, Scotland, EH20 9EA Tel/Fax 0131 440 0751
Workshop at home, five miles from centre of Edinburgh; visitors welcome by appointment

Paul Priest

The work is handbuilt, human and animal subjects, although some thrown work is included. Pieces are kiln-fired, some using raku, some fired then broken and reconstructed as the mask illustrates. I am also involved with workshops and demonstrations as well as exhibitions etc.

71 Sunnycroft, Downley, High Wycombe, Buckinghamshire, HP13 5UR
Tel 01494 639819 Fax 01494 639951 Email paulwpriest@aol.com

Jacqui Ramrayka

Jacqui Ramrayka trained at the University of Westminster, Harrow. She graduated in 1994, gaining a BA(Hons) in Ceramics. Before embarking on this course she travelled extensively around south east Asia and the Caribbean; these experiences have been a great influence on her work. Currently she works from her studio – a converted railway arch in the East End of London – which she set up with three other potters after leaving college. From here she produces a range of mainly thrown ceramics, working in series and making one-off pieces, using richly textured and vibrantly coloured glazes.

Archway Ceramics, 410 Haven Mews, 23 St Paul's Way, London E3 4AG Tel 020 8983 1323
Mobile 07973 771687 Email info@jacquiramrayka.com Website www.jacquiramrayka.com

Jacqueline Rankin

Clay has a wonderful tactile quality, both in its raw state and in the many ways it can be formed by hand and machine. My work, mainly sculptural, focuses on form and surface, but most importantly on the sensory quality of clay: seeing, touching and hearing. Wherever possible I encourage a hands-on experience or a space for listening. A body of work developed over the last ten years ranges from small, tactile hand-held forms to larger garden sculptures, installations and water fountains. Inspirations and influences have come from family members and friends who have touched my life in a very special way. Part of my interest in working with clay is to encourage others from all aspects of the community to learn and enjoy new skills through engaging in creative events, whilst developing new ideas in my own working practice.

Jacqueline Rankin Sculptural Ceramics, 45 West View Road, Sutton Coldfield, West Midlands, B75 6AZ
Tel 0121 378 1844 Email jrsceramics@btinternet.com

Nick Rees Fellow

Nick Rees has successfully established an individual style to his work during a career that has spanned over thirty years. The Leach tradition has given a clear foundation with technique, form and process learned through working at Muchelney Pottery. Nick's personal pieces also showcase a subtle and refined approach to shape and design, accentuated through carving, fluting and experimentation with slips and glazes. This surface detail combined with the uniqueness afforded by the wood firing process, allows Nick to produce a range of work that is both distinctive and organic.

MUCHELNEY

Muchelney Pottery, Muchelney, Nr Langport, Somerset, TA10 0DW
Tel 01458 250324

Petra Reynolds

Petra Reynolds graduated from Cardiff in 1995 and has since lived and worked at Wobage Farm Craft Workshops, Herefordshire. Using paper templates, clay slabs are deftly cut, bent up and joined to form a wide range of domestic pots, including serving dishes, drinking beakers, jugs, vases and teapots. Surface imagery is built up using a combination of brushwork, blocks of paper resist and printed line. Pots are raw-glazed and once-fired to 1300°C with soda in wood-fired kilns.

Wobage Farm, Upton Bishop, Ross-on-Wye, Herefordshire, HR9 7QP Tel 01989 780448
Fax 01989 780495 Wobage Makers Gallery open Apr-Sept: Thurs-Sun 10am-5pm;
Oct-Mar: Sat-Sun only; other times by appointment only

Mary Rich Fellow

Mary Rich has been working as a full-time
potter in Cornwall since 1962. The work is
hand-thrown porcelain, mostly decorated
with liquid bright gold and lustres. A member of the Devon Guild of Craftsmen and the
Cornwall Crafts Association.

Penwerris Pottery, Cowlands Creek, Old Kea, Nr Truro, Cornwall, TR3 6AT Tel 01872 276926
Visitors are welcome to visit the workshop; please telephone first for directions

The Ceramics Book | 219

Christine-Ann Richards Fellow

Christine-Ann Richards, whose pots reflect an Eastern aesthetic, has worked in thrown porcelain for three decades specialising in crackle and monochrome glazes. Trained at Harrow School of Art (1971-3) under Mick Casson, she worked for David Leach before founding her first workshop within the Barbican Arts Group (1975-83). Works alone. The 1978 CPA trip to China had a radical effect on her work and life. She pursued Chinese studies and over twenty years has organised visits to artists, archaeological sites and places of cultural interest in China and Central Asia. For more than a decade she has been making large pots, water features and sculptures for the garden. A Winston Churchill Travelling Fellowship to Japan in 1996 to 'look at the way that water is used in landscape and architecture' has been a source of inspiration for these works. Works to commission.

CAR

Chapel House, High Street, Wanstrow, Nr Shepton Mallet, Somerset, BA4 4TE Tel/Fax 01749 850208
Email mail@christineannrichards.co.uk Website www.christineannrichards.co.uk Visitors welcome by appointment

Audrey Richardson

Audrey Richardson trained originally in painting and sculpture at Duncan of Jordanstone College of Art, Dundee, Scotland. Started potting through attending local evening classes. Works alone, making individual pots and sculptures. These are handbuilt using mainly T material, then decorated with a selected range of slips and glazes. The work is fired to 1250°C. Also undertakes large garden sculptures and por-

traits on commission. Has idyllic garden workshop overlooking the sea.

Morawel, Parrog Road, Newport, Pembrokeshire, SA42 0RF
Tel 01239 820449 Visitors welcome by appointment

David Roberts Fellow

David Roberts is well known for his large-scale, coil-built, raku-fired ceramics. His work has been exhibited throughout the UK and abroad and is represented in many UK and international public collections. Workshops and demonstrations held frequently in the UK and Europe. In 2000 a monograph, *Tainting With Smoke*, was published on his work. At present setting up a second studio in northern Tuscany. David

Roberts is a member of the International Academy of Ceramics.

UK: Cressfield House, 44 Upperthong Lane, Holmfirth, Huddersfield, Yorkshire, HD9 3BQ Tel 01484 685110
Italy: 14 Via Castello, Castello de Comano, 54015 Comano, MS, Italy Mobile +44 (0) 7985 021111
Email david@davidroberts-ceramics.com Website www.davidroberts-ceramics.com

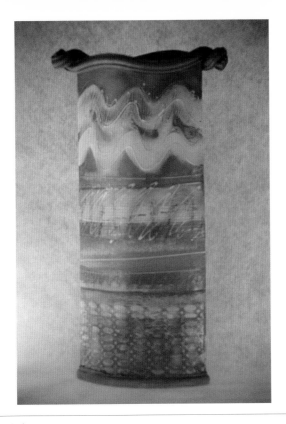

Jim Robison Fellow

As a practitioner, time is divided between sculptural forms, domestic pottery and commissioned works. Best known for large-scale slab ware, planters, garden pots and architectural panels, the studio (Booth House Gallery and Pottery), founded in 1975, contains regular exhibitions of finished work and is open to the public. Vases and bowls are rich in detail, with combinations of textures, coloured slips and reduction glazes fired in a large gas kiln. He is also author of many articles and the book *Large-scale Ceramics* (A&C Black, 1997).

Booth House Gallery, 3 Booth House, Holmfirth, Huddersfield, HD9 2QT Tel/Fax 01484 685270
Email jim.robison@virgin.net Website www.jimrobison.co.uk or www.boothhousegallery.co.uk

Emma Rodgers Fellow

Confrontation, energy, curiosity, essence of a moment and interaction are the main elements that initially draw me to a new subject and are indicative of the very nature of the animals I have depicted. It is not purely an interest in animals, but the challenges of capturing the inherent nature of the subject, particularly where the movement, flexibility and power of the animal is concerned. Emma Rodgers studied for both her BA (Hons) and MA at Wolverhampton University. She has exhibited worldwide, including Victoria and Albert Museum, Cork Street, Royal Academy of Art, London; Lineart, Ghent; and SOFA, Chicago. She has been featured in a documentary dedicated to her work on the Artsworld Channel. National Museums and Galleries purchased Rodgers's work for their collection in 2003. She has received acclaim for her energy and dynamic approach to her work.

12 Birch Road, Oxton, Wirral, Cheshire, CH43 5UA Tel/Fax 0151 652 3040
Website www.emmarodgers.co.uk Studio not open to public

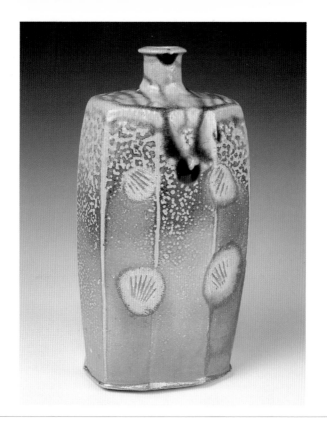

Phil Rogers Fellow

Born in 1951. Came to live and work in mid Wales in 1977, and moved to present site in 1984. Most pots are thrown with an increasing number press-moulded. I have three kilns – a gas-fired salt kiln, an oil-fired reduction kiln and a two-chambered wood-fired kiln. I make use of as many local materials as possible for the glazes and slips. Exhibited in many galleries in the UK and overseas, particularly the USA. My work is represented in thirty-six museums including the Victoria and Albert Museum, National Museum of Wales, Boston Museum of Fine Art, Detroit Institute of Art and the World Ceramic Centre in Korea. Past Chair of the Craft Potters Association, member of the International Academy of Ceramics, the Royal Cambrian Academy and the Crafts Council Index of Selected Makers. Author of *Ash Glazes*, *Salt Glazing* and *Throwing Pots* (all A&C Black).

Marston Pottery, Lower Cefn Faes, Rhayader, Powys, LD6 5LT Tel 01597 810875
Email phil@marstonpottery.wanadoo.co.uk Website www.philrogerspottery.com
Opening hours Mon-Sun 9.30am-5.30pm; please telephone if coming a long distance

Duncan Ross Fellow

Duncan Ross established his studio near Farnham in 1989 after a period of exploration into terra sigillata techniques. His work is represented in many important public and private collections including the Victoria and Albert and Fitzwilliam Museums. He is on the Crafts Council Index of Selected Makers. His work is thrown and burnished using many layers of a fine terra sigillata slip with resist and inlay decoration. Colours are achieved by smoke firing. He aims to develop a rich surface integral to the clay that has a feeling of depth, allowing the smoke process to play its essential and unpredictable part.

Daneshay House, 69A Alma Lane, Upper Hale, Farnham, Surrey, GU9 OLT Tel 01252 710704
Email duncan@duncanrossceramics.co.uk Website www.duncanrossceramics.co.uk
Visitors to studio showroom welcome by appointment

Elisabeth Roussel

Trained at Antioch University (USA) and Goldsmiths College (In Service Diploma, London University, 1985). Member of Oxfordshire Craft Guild. Concentrates mainly on wheel-thrown stoneware and porcelain bowls, vases and plates fired in reduction to 1285°C. Each pot is a one-off and often made to commission. The pieces are richly decorated with motifs drawn from nature. The work is particularly suitable for com-memorative occasions where calligraphy becomes an integral part of the design.

26 High Street, Woodstock, Oxfordshire, OX20 1TG Tel 01993 811298
Email leroussel@aol.com Visitors welcome by appointment

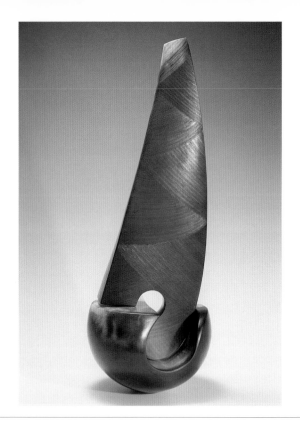

Antonia Salmon Fellow

Antonia Salmon is known for her fine burnished and smoke-fired sculpture and pots.
Her interest is in expressing a centredness
and dynamism within each abstract work;
creating contemplative forms that sit with
poise. Work is represented in private and
public collections in Great Britain, Europe,
USA and Canada.

20 Adelaide Road, Nether Edge, Sheffield, S7 1SQ Tel 0114 258 5971
Email antoniasalmon@hemscott.net Website www.antoniasalmon-ceramics.co.uk Visitors welcome by appointment

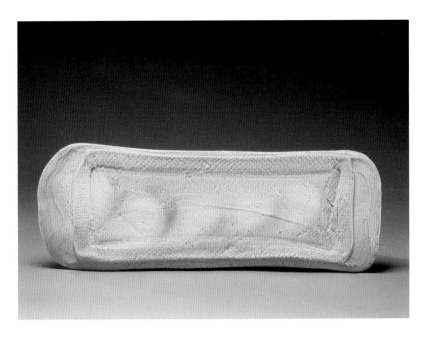

Robert Sanderson Fellow

I have been involved with wood firing ever
since I left college in 1975. Currently living
in Ireland with my wife Coll Minogue, we edit
and publish *The Log Book* – the international
publication for wood-fired ceramics. We also
wrote *Wood-fired Ceramics: Contemporary
Practices* (A&C Black, 2000). Recent wood-fire
kiln building workshops include Rufford
Crafts Centre, Nottinghamshire, England; Red
Deer College, Alberta, Canada. Grants: British

Council; British American Arts Association.
Awards: Scottish Arts Council Crafts Bursary
1994; Winston Churchill Travelling Fellowship
1997. Founding member of ICMEA –
International Ceramic Magazine Editors
Association. Over the years my work has
evolved to reflect that spontaneity only
found by firing with wood; accepting the
unpredictable and anticipating the unknown.

PO Box 612, Scariff, County Clare, Republic of Ireland Tel/Fax +353 (0) 61 922918
Email thelogbook@eircom.net Website www.thelogbook.net

Micki Schloessingk Fellow

Micki Schloessingk trained in studio pottery at Harrow and has been exploring the relationship between wood firing and salt glazing ever since. She established her present studio on the Gower Peninsular in 1987. Micki makes a range of individual and functional pots both wheel-based and handbuilt. She runs summer courses at Bridge Pottery as well as giving workshops and demonstrations in Britain and abroad.

Micki has exhibited widely and her work is in many private and public collections.

Bridge Pottery, Cheriton, Nr Llanmadoc, Gower, Swansea, SA3 1BY Tel 01792 386499
Email micki@mickisaltglaze.co.uk Website www.mickisaltglaze.co.uk
Visitors welcome most Fri-Sat 10am-5pm and often at other times; please phone to check (closed January)

David Scott Fellow

Born in Yorkshire and studied at Stoke-on-Trent and the Royal College of Art. Programme leader for Ceramics at Loughborough University School of Art and Design. Currently the work focuses on interpretations of functional vessel forms with reference to a variety of traditions.

David Scott

22B Manor Road, Loughborough, Leicestershire, LE11 2LY
Tel 01509 228955 Email d.scott1@lboro.ac.uk

Claire Seneviratne

My work explores the balance and juxtapositions of form, colour and texture and how these elements relate to the mind. Many influences from the natural world such as fossils and landscapes inspire my work but it is primarily abstract and symbolises the concepts elaborated below. The forms are fluid and symmetrical, rising up from a base indicating growth. This represents how we structure our minds using values as an anchor to balance

our lives and promote spiritual development. Colour connects to our emotional life. An awareness of our emotions leads to greater clarity. A textural veil of random marks floating on selected areas of the form is reminiscent of our spontaneous thought process: a continuous stream of ideas which can be guided into a positive creative energy. My ceramic jewellery explores similar ideas; an aesthetically balanced union between the elements.

15 Romeo Arbour, Heathcote, Warwick Gates, Warwick, CV34 6FD Tel 01926 426006
Email claire@seneviratne.co.uk Website www.claire.seneviratne.co.uk Visitors welcome by appointment

Kathy Shadwell

Kathy Shadwell studied at Goldsmiths College, London, where she obtained a post-graduate Diploma in Ceramics and was commended by the board of examiners. Prior to this she took an HNC in Industrial Ceramic Design. In 2001 she was elected as a professional member of The Craft Potters Association. Her work is figurative and partly influenced by earlier years spent in nursing. She uses female forms to depict feelings and emotions. The figures are made from sheets of laminated clays including porcelain and fired in a gas kiln to a temperature of 1260°C. Her work ranges in size from 25-150cm. Larger pieces are suitable for gardens. Kathy has been involved in international workshops in Japan and Germany, exhibiting there and in New Zealand and Spain as well as in the UK. Her work is in private collections in Europe, America and Singapore.

24 Priory Avenue, North Cheam, Surrey, SM3 8LX Tel 020 8644 7471
Email jrwhiting@tiscali.co.uk Visitors welcome by appointment

Jeremy Sharp

The bulk of my work is lead-glazed slipware. The forms are simple and restrained and inspired by the functional domestic earthenware of the country potteries of the late nineteenth and early twentieth centuries. Two main clays are used, a red terracotta body dipped in white ball clay slip and fired under a rich honey glaze (see photo). The other is a white earthenware clay loosely decorated with coloured slips and fired with a clear lead glaze. Although the simpler forms may be raw-glazed, most of the work is biscuit-fired and then glaze-fired to 1130°C in an electric kiln.

1 Lychpole Farm Cottages, Titch Hill, Sompting, West Sussex, BN15 0AY Tel 01903 763021
Email jay@lychpolefarm.fsnet.co.uk Visitors welcome by appointment

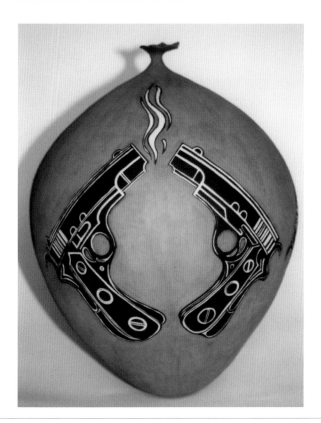

Georgia Shearman

I build my pots with coils of red earthenware clay, then burnish the surface, which smooths and partially seals the pot. I then decorate the surface by painting on velvet underglaze colours, then once-fire at 1060°C. *Impervious to Bullets* (illustrated) was inspired by a poster saying 'If you were found with a gun... what would happen?' I was thinking, if I had a gun how many people I may have shot, in moments of rage,

just saying, how much working out we need to do together to stop the shooting. I once used pure decoration; now I am drawing on actual objects – e.g. spoons, labels, shiny-looking watches – and using this ancient form to hold and contain meaning.

27 Stevens Crescent, Tatterdown, Bristol, BS3 4UH
Tel 0117 971 0071

Shelton Pottery

Ken and Valerie Shelton make their pottery in partnership at their Cheshire studio. Ken makes the pottery, mostly vases and bowls in white earthenware. The pots are thrown and turned to produce a characteristic lightweight and smooth surface that is ready to be painted. Ken combines the pottery with work in the kiln manufacturing industry. Valerie's painting is all done free-hand using underglaze colours; the work reflects her training in fashion and textiles at Brighton and Bristol art colleges. She has always been fascinated by the inter-relationship of colours and the form and texture of brush-stroke. Her painting is usually of flowers and fruit, sometimes with abstract effects and always with bright colours merging and overlapping to give great depth to the design. Work is sold in galleries throughout the UK.

Valerie Shelton

18 Heath End Road, Alsager, Cheshire, ST7 2SQ
Tel/Fax 01270 872686 Email sheltonpottery@aol.com

Alan Sidney Fellow

Romps into fantasy, rich in symbolism, each
part-questioned thoroughly in relation to
the whole. Alan Sidney's pieces have steadily
evolved over the past thirty years and each
is a celebration of the versatility of the
medium of ceramics. He has exhibited widely in Britain and Europe.

Minhafren Mill, Aberbechan, Newtown, Powys, SY16 3AW
Tel 01686 630644

Ray Silverman Fellow

Trained at Camberwell School of Art and
Crafts and University of London Goldsmiths
College. Fellow of the Society of Designer-
Craftsmen and on the Crafts Council Index
of Selected Makers. Exhibited widely in solo
and groups exhibitions throughout the
world. His work has ranged from thrown
tableware and handbuilt pieces to working
as a designer and consultant in the ceramic
industry. He now devotes time to producing
individual thrown forms in porcelain and
stoneware.

29 Wordsworth Gardens, Borehamwood, Hertfordshire, WD6 2AB Tel/Fax 020 8905 2441
Mobile 07747 636772 Email raymondsilverman@hotmail.com Visitors welcome by appointment

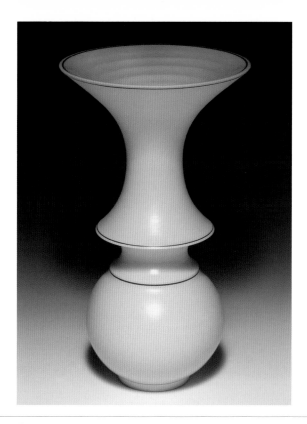

Anna Silverton

Anna Silverton's vases and bowls are wheel-thrown. Rhythmic structures are interrupted and repeated through cutting, joining and reshaping on the wheel. She places particular importance on the ceramic surface and its relationship with form, using a combination of incised and/or inlaid detailing to enhance volume and punctuate profile. The quality and colour of the unglazed ceramic body is highlighted through burnishing (low-fired clay bodies such as dark brown earthenware) or polishing (vitrified stoneware bodies such as cream stoneware). The insides of the cream stoneware vases are glazed, primarily for practical purposes but also to highlight the rippled softness of the throwing rings in contrast to the smooth stone-like exterior. (Photo: Andra Nelki)

41 Burghill Road, Sydenham, London, SE26 4HJ Tel 020 8659 0767
Email annasilverton@hotmail.com Visitors welcome by appointment

Penny Simpson

Penny Simpson started making pots during a three-year stay in Japan. She is the author of *The Japanese Pottery Handbook* (Kodansha, 1979). From 1979-81 Penny trained at Dartington Pottery in Devon. She uses red earthenware clay decorated with coloured slips to produce a range of hand-thrown pots including bowls, jugs, plates, lamp-bases and plant pots. She also decorates tiles, making panels for kitchens and bathrooms as well as a range of individual tiles.

The Studio, 44A Court Street, Moretonhampstead, Devon, TQ13 8LG Tel/Fax 01647 440708
Email psimpson@thestudiopots.fsnet.co.uk Workshop and showroom open to visitors, Mon-Fri 9.30am-5pm
and some weekends; telephone first if making special journey

Daniel Smith

Daniel Smith graduated from Harrow College
in 1994 and produces a wide range of hand-
thrown porcelain tableware. His honest and
simple approach results in an understated
elegance. The weight of the porcelain in the
hand combined with the pure delicate form
makes each piece a delight to hold and use.

DS

Archway Ceramics, 410 Haven Mews, 23 St Paul's Way, London, E3 4AG Tel 020 8983 1323
Email danielsmith@w3e3.freeserve.co.uk

Elizabeth Smith

I use white bone china clay to make strong elegant forms complemented by sensuously burnished and textured surfaces that explore pattern and light. Pattern making is one of the central creative processes I employ in making unusual delicate hangings, lights and vessels. Various patterns and textures radically transform thinly rolled or thrown clay into richly decorated surfaces. These are embellished with impressed designs on soft clay using hand-carved and modelled stamps, textured papers or fabric. I am motivated to search for ways in which the form, function and patterns might evolve to enhance the translucent qualities of the fired clay. I graduated in ceramics, stone carving and sculpture at Leicester and have enjoyed a long career lecturing in ceramics, art and theatre design and now work to commission and sell my ceramics through galleries and craft fairs.

Millhead House, Millhead, Bampton, Nr Tiverton, Devon, EX16 9LP Tel/Fax 01398 331442
Email smithmillhead@aol.com Visitors are welcome at my display studio and workshop by appointment

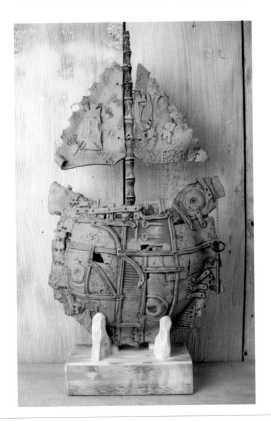

Mark Smith

All my work draws inspiration from the sea and each piece is uniquely different. When I produce a piece of work it reflects a journey, a form of storytelling. Found objects, either from the sea or on the mainland, almost always become part of the story. A variety of decoration techniques are used and ideas continue to flow and move on to create different avenues and new approaches. Ships, boats and wrecks are the main fabric of the work, having been made from clay that, with textures of metal and wood objects, salvaged, press-moulded and patched together, produce a variety of forms that look as though they have sailed the seven seas.

11 School Lane, Sudbury, Ashbourne, Derbyshire, DE6 5HZ
Tel 01283 585219 Visitors welcome by appointment

Peter Smith Fellow

The work illustrated, *Drawing No. 8,* is made
from industrial castable refractory and is
high-fired. It is surfaced with slip and other
familiar ceramic materials. This piece represents my current interests which are ceramic
but experimental.

Higher Bojewyan, Pendeen, Penzance, Cornwall, TR19 7TR
Tel 01736 788820 Email petersmith1@lineone.net Visitors welcome by appointment

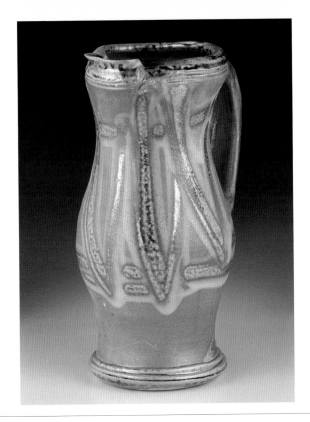

Jeremy Steward Fellow

I make kitchen, table and oven ware which fits comfortably into everyday use in the home. The pots are thrown on a momentum wheel. They are decorated with finger-wiped slips or embellished with a stamp or wooden roulette, providing movement and accentuation to form. The insides are raw-glazed and the pots once-fired to about 1300°C (Orton cone 12) with soda in wood firing kilns.

Wobage Farm, Upton Bishop, Ross-on-Wye, Herefordshire, HR9 7QP Tel 01989 780448
Fax 01989 780495 Wobage Makers Gallery open Apr-Sept: Thurs-Sun 10am-5pm;
Oct-Mar: Sat-Sun only; other times by appointment only

Geoffrey Swindell Fellow

I have been working on a miniature scale, making porcelain vessels, normally less than 12cm high, since graduating from the Royal College of Art in 1970. The form appears to be a synthesis of organic and mechanical images – accurately engineered shapes made on the potter's wheel with physically or visually textured surfaces that parallel natural qualities. My work has been included in many international exhibitions and publica-tions with solo shows in London and New York. Examples are held in numerous private collections and over thirty museums throughout the world including the Victoria and Albert Museum, London.

18 Laburnum Way, Dinas Powys, Vale of Glamorgan, CF64 4TH Email geoff@dell18.freeserve.co.uk
Website www.geoffreyswindellceramics.co.uk Visitors welcome by appointment

Nicola Tassie

I work in thrown domestic ware, making a selected range of forms consisting of carafes, bottles, flat-bottomed bowls and jugs. My ideas are centred on concerns about surface and its relation to form, using restrained satin tin-glazes over regular incised grooves, inlay lines or crosshatchings. This is extended by combining matt and shiny surfaces, and an exploration of colour using poured slips. Alongside the functional ceramics I create 'still life' groups of bottles and jars that integrate the practice of sculpture, ceramics and painting. The surface treatment imitates and at times confounds the effects of transparency or shadows in order to flatten the three-dimensional assemblage, converting them into two-dimensional compositions. I work from my studio in east London.

Standpoint Studios, 45 Coronet Street, London, N1 6HD Tel 020 7729 5292
Fax 020 7739 4921 Visitors welcome by appointment

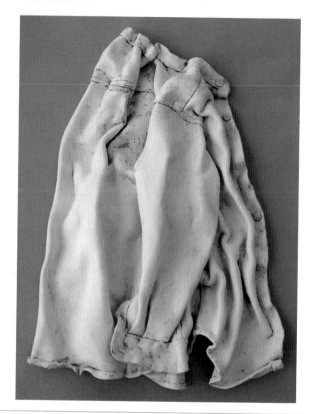

Kaori Tatebayashi

I use clay as a device to make fragments of time visible. I want to preserve the intimate and transient recollections of our lives and seal them in the clay like a fern petrified into a fossil. Firing changes soft, malleable clay into hard, breakable ceramic. As clay loses its organic life in the firing, it allows time to become encased. The nature of fired clay incorporates both fragility and permanence and it is this which enables the material to record elusive things like memory. I trace everyday objects in clay. Through looking at my work, you are back into those tiny, quiet recesses of your past.

401½ Workshops, 401½ Wandsworth Road, London, SW8 2JP Mobile 07816 422033 Email info@kaoriceramics.com
Website www.kaoriceramics.com Opening hours Mon-Fri 10am-6pm; visitors by appointment only

Rebecca Taylor

Rebecca Taylor creates mainly wall-mounted
sculptural forms, heavily textured and suitable
for both interior and exterior use. She also
designs tiling for bathrooms, kitchens and
courtyards to specific designs that simulate
beaches, waterfalls and stone slabs etc. A documentary was made about Rebecca for
Artsworld, a copy of which is available on
request. She is now working on giant totem
poles of combined ceramic, glass and concrete.

rt
POTS

Home: 18 Clarion House, St Anne's Court, Soho, London, W1F 0BA Tel 020 7434 2924
Studio: Goodlands Cottage, Botany Bay Lane, Chislehurst, Kent, BR7 5PT Mobile 07960 942007

Yo Thom

Born in Tokyo, Japan. After her degree in English Language, she moved to the UK in 1996. Obtained MA in Ceramics (2000), and worked as an apprentice for Lisa Hammond before she established her own studio in 2004. Yo's work is mainly wheel-thrown functional stoneware and one-off vessels. Round and soft forms, and the grey and orange carbon-trapped shino glaze are characteristic of her work. Her work also has a unique fusion of British and Japanese influence in its form and its use.

A115 Faircharm Studios, 8-12 Creekside, Deptford, London, SE8 3DX Tel 020 8305 8427
Email yodekune@hotmail.com Visitors welcome by appointment; opening hours 10am-5pm

Owen Thorpe Fellow

Owen Thorpe started pottery in London in 1970, moving to Shropshire in 1975 and Churchstoke, Powys, in 1981. Works alone. Produces a range of domestic stoneware using coloured and local clay slips and wax-resist decoration. All work is wheel-thrown and is fired with electric oxidising firing. Also produces a range of garden pottery decorated using coloured slips. Also makes highly decorated individual pieces using a technique like majolica but at stoneware temperatures. Tin glazes are employed, some tinted cream or light blue with elaborate brushed patterns applied to the unfired glaze. This process is also employed in producing celebration ware for anniversaries, presentations, weddings etc. in which majolica decoration is combined with calligraphy. Recent work tends to be more sculptural, based on horse images and figurework.

Priestweston Pottery, The Chapel, Priestweston, Chirbury, Montgomery, Powys, SY15 6DE
Tel 01938 561618 Visitors welcome by appointment

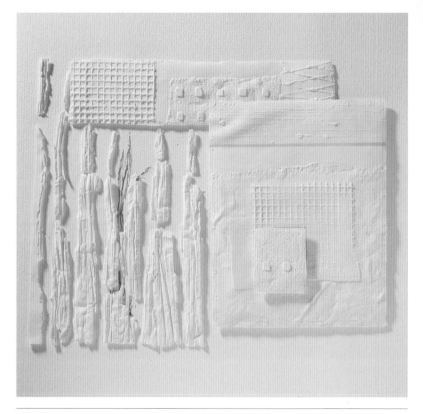

Deborah Timperley

Deborah Timperley is an artist who makes bone china framed compositions and sculptural pieces mounted on plinths. Two of her favourite materials – fabric and plaster – are used in the process. Either plaster casts are taken from fabric compositions and then cast in bone china slip or fabric is drawn through the slip then hung to dry and fired. Colour is used minimally. Some pieces are abstract, the composition derived from the juxtaposition of the surface details of the fabric, while others explore drapes, folds and creases, sometimes in the form of dresses. Deborah gained her degree at Middlesex University in glass and ceramics. She still works with both materials, using fabric as a major element. The methods for glass are more process-orientated, contrasting with the more spontaneous approach employed for the bone china pieces.

59 Smithbarn, Horsham, West Sussex, RH13 6DT Tel 01403 265835 Email deborah.timperley@btinternet.com
Website www.studiopottery.co.uk or www.portfoliocity.com/deborahtimperley Visitors welcome by appointment

Fran Tristram

My work is largely wheel-thrown but includes a range of hand-built domestic pieces. My current glaze palette is drawn from the idyllic coastal landscapes of my Irish childhood – warm earthy colours, inspired by the action of weather on surface. While I love working in stoneware for its unashamedly earthy sense of itself I also admire the refinement of porcelain and seek to achieve something of that refinement in my handling of the stoneware clay on the wheel. The constant stretching to master the skills of making is a great springboard to creativity. Function is an important aspect of my work and I enjoy and celebrate the domestic in terms both of use, context and scale – the domestic is the central core of everyday life and as such can speak directly and universally to all.

Lady Bay Pottery, 42 Seymour Road, West Bridgford, Nottingham, NG2 5EF Tel 0115 982 2681
Email frantristram@ntlworld.com Website www.nottinghamstudios.org.uk/ladybay Visitors welcome by appointment

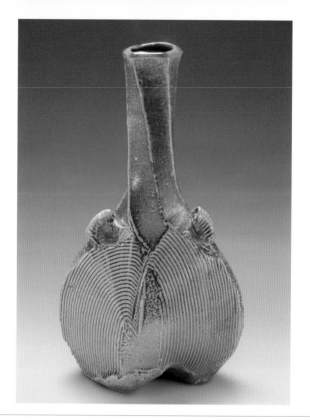

Ruthanne Tudball Fellow

All of my work is once-fired stoneware with some porcelain, slip decorated and sodium vapour glazed with bicarbonate of soda in a gas/wood kiln. Drawing inspiration from rhythms and movement in the natural world as well as the human body, I make functional and some more contemplative work that celebrates the soft plasticity of clay. I have made a number of lecture tours of the UK, North America, Europe and Australasia and have written the book *Soda Glazing* (A&C Black, 1995). My work is in public and private collections in England, Europe, North America and Japan.

Temple Barn Pottery, Solomon's Temple, Welborne, Dereham, Norfolk, NR20 3LD Tel 01362 858770
Email ruthanne@ruthannetudball.com or ruthanne_tudball@btopenworld.com Website www.ruthannetudball.com
Visitors are welcome to my studio and showroom all year round, but advisable to telephone first

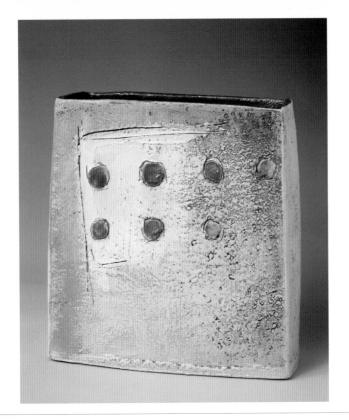

Craig Underhill

Craig Underhill's work reflects his interest in the visual contrasts that are created through the influence of mankind on the natural landscape and of nature on the man-made landscape. He uses drawing and painting as a method of exploring and developing ideas before ceramic pieces are made. Forms are constructed with slabs and vary in size from small pieces 15-20cm high to more monumental pieces 70-80cm high. Surfaces are built up in stages using combinations of incised lines, slips and glazes, which are applied with a balance of spontaneity and knowledge from past experience.

8 Prescot Road, Stourbridge, West Midlands, DY9 7LD Tel 01384 376559
Email craigunderhill@waitrose.com Visitors welcome by appointment

Sue Varley

I studied at the Bath Academy of Art, Corsham, where I was taught by James Tower. I am mainly inspired by looking at natural phenomena. For example, shadows and ripples on the surface of water, changing colours and patterns of moving clouds. The forms and tones of pebbles, stones and strata. All my work is handbuilt. I make pinched bowls inspired by landscape and, more recently, I have been making flattish slab dishes and platters. I mix metal oxides into the main clay body and also use coloured slips which may be burnished before firing. The work is then fired to 960°C in an electric kiln and then post-fired in newspaper or sawdust to create areas of reduction.

SV

54 Elthorne Road, Uxbridge, Middlesex, UB8 2PS Tel 01895 231738
Email suevarley@btconnect.com Visitors welcome by appointment

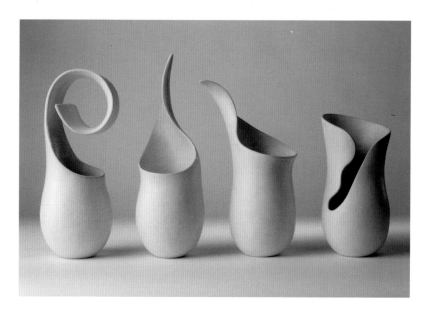

Tina Vlassopulos Fellow

Individual pieces made from burnished red
earthenware or coloured clays.

29 Canfield Gardens, London, NW6 3JP Tel 020 7624 4582
Fax 020 7328 1483 Email tina@4tuna.fsnet.co.uk Visitors welcome by appointment

Motoko Watana

Born in Tokyo. Started potting in Japan then
been working in the UK since 1999. Now
makes slip-decorated stoneware in St Ives.

Gaolyard Studios, Dove Street, St Ives, Cornwall, TR26 2LZ Tel 01736 799336
Email wakanamoto@hotmail.com Website www.gaolyard-studio-pottery.co.uk

Clare Wakefield

In 1991 Clare Wakefield graduated from Cardiff with a BA Hons in Ceramics following the OND course at KIAD in 1989. Plant, human and animal life are all evident in her sculptural pieces. At present muscle fibres, tendons and skeletal structure all feature strongly. Handbuilding and throwing are the main processes used in producing the sculptures, although pinching, slab building and pulling are also used. The work is fired to 1200°C in an electric kiln after having first been through a 1000°C bisque. The predominant use of blue and white glazes reflect Clare's fascination with the sea; they also help to complement the flow and energy she strives for within her work.
(Photo: Anna Fitzmaurice)

10 Station Road, Walmer, Deal, Kent, CT14 7QR Tel 01304 239771
Email clarewakefield@aol.com Website www.clarewakefield.co.uk Visitors welcome by appointment

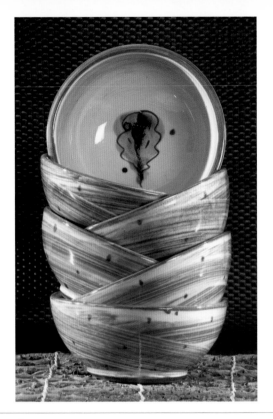

Josie Walter Fellow

Born 1951. Trained as an anthropologist, then as a teacher and finally as a potter on the studio ceramics course, Chesterfield College of Art (1976-9). After six months as a repetition thrower with Suzie Atkins at Le Don Pottery, Auvergne, France, shared a workshop with John Gibson for eight years, followed by ten years in an old mill. The workshop is now next to the house. Over the past few years I have experimented with paper resist and slips poured onto the clay surfaces to create overlapping layers or applied thickly with large brushes to wrap slip around the pots. Recent work has explored the effects of coloured glazes. All the work is once-fired to cone 3.

22 Nan Gells Hill, Bolehill, Derbyshire, DE4 4GN Tel/Fax 01629 823669
Email josie@josiewalter.co.uk Website www.josiewalter.co.uk Visitors welcome by appointment

Sarah Walton Fellow

Sarah Walton has run a pottery in Sussex since 1975, using a large oil-fired salt kiln. She works alone, though supported by part-time assistants. She studied fine art at Chelsea from 1960-4 and studio pottery at Harrow from 1971-3. Landscape is a theme in her work. She has walked, drawn and painted landscape since childhood and this lies behind her evolution of birdbaths, which she has made since 1984 and that now dominate her output. She presently makes a few pots, pinched or press-moulded rather than thrown. Her pots are represented in thirteen museums in this country. The wall and floor tiles she makes can only be seen by visiting the pottery.

Keeper's, Bo-Peep Lane, Alciston, Nr Polegate, East Sussex, BN26 6UH Tel/Fax 01323 811517
Email sarah.walton@freenet.co.uk Website www.sarahwalton.co.uk
The pottery is open 11am-5pm weekdays, weekends by appointment; advisable to telephone in advance.

John Ward Fellow

Born in London, 1938. Studied ceramics at Camberwell School of Arts and Crafts (1966–70). Set-up first workroom in 1970 and taught part-time at an adult education institute until 1979 before moving to Wales to pot full-time. Central theme is simple hollow forms, often derived from the bowl and usually decorated, either with a black and white design or simple abstract designs using blue, green and ochre slip glazes. All pots are fired to 1250°C in an electric kiln; those with coloured slip glazes are once-fired.

Fachongle Uchaf, Cilgwyn, Newport, Pembrokeshire, SA42 0QR Tel 01239 820706
Email john@ward-wales.freeserve.co.uk Visitors welcome by appointment

Sasha Wardell Fellow

Born 1956 in Sri Lanka. Studied ceramics at Bath Academy of Art (1976-9), North Staffordshire Polytechnic (1979-81) and Ecole Nationale d'Art Decoratifs in Limoges, France. Has taught in various art colleges since 1981 and set up workshop, exhibiting in the UK and abroad since 1982. Materials and processes involve slipcasting bone china to an eggshell thinness to enhance translucency. Author of *Slipcasting* (A&C Black, 1997) and *Porcelain and Bone China* (Crowood Press, 2004).

36 Tory, Bradford on Avon, Wiltshire, BA15 1NN Tel 01225 868756 Mobile 07855 110603
Email swardell@dircon.co.uk Website www.studiopottery.co.uk Visitors welcome by appointment

Annette Welch

My studio is located at the bottom of the garden. Its location directly influences my ceramics as a passion for plants has become an essential source. A recent series of dishes, bowls and platters reflect this horticultural influence and fascination with the idiosyncrasies in nature. Leaves directly plucked from my garden form textural decoration and pattern. Large platters have dominant characteristics, the surfaces treated as a bold canvas with heavily veined imprints. The smaller dishes have a more ephemeral character as the leaf impressions form shadows which drift across the surface. Forms are explored through a variety of ceramic processes: wheel-thrown, press-moulded and pinched, all cut and altered. Resist techniques are used with slip and glaze washes, all stoneware fired to 1270°C.

21 Colyton Road, East Dulwich, London, SE22 ONE
Tel 020 8693 9400 Email annettewelch@mac.com

Nicola Werner

Nicola Werner studied painting at Central School of Art in London, trained at Aldermaston Pottery for four years with Alan Caiger-Smith and Edgar Campden and set up her own studio in 1986. Since then she has been prolific, producing a wide range of domestic ware and tiles, selling them through galleries across the UK, sales and fairs, direct from the workshop in Devon and by post via her website. She throws in Brannam's Fremington clay and makes up a rich creamy tin glaze on which she paints flowing leaf and bird patterns and fires slowly in two electric kilns. European majolica is her main influence, coupled with a love of nature and a desire to make everyday life more colourful and enjoyable, whether it be the mug one drinks from or the kitchen tiles.

· NW·V·

Nicola Werner Pottery, Burcombe Farm, Bolham Water, Clayhidon, Nr Cullompton, Devon, EX15 3QB
Tel 01823 680957 Website www.nicolawerner.com

Gilda Westermann Fellow

Gilda Westermann makes finely thrown porcelain tableware and vessels. She is known for a quality of throwing which is fluent, soft and intuitive. Gilda has been a potter for twenty years, training in Stuttgart, Ireland and London. Her work is held in the British Council collection and private collections. The current range of porcelain pots includes domestic items such as mugs, tea bowls, jugs, sets of bowls to eat from and large salad bowls to serve with at the table. She also creates angular dishes, decorated with liquid porcelain and gold and amber lustre, painted with expressive marks and compositions. Her recent works include beautiful large centrepieces in thrown porcelain, sculptural vessels and platters. 'My wish is to offer pots which people can enjoy, treasure and celebrate. Pots which bring beauty and harmony to the home and are always present as good friends.'

2 The Shrubbery, Topsham, Exeter, EX3 ODW Tel 01392 873622 Email g.westermann@freeuk.com
Website www.g.westermann.freeuk.com Visitors welcome by appointment

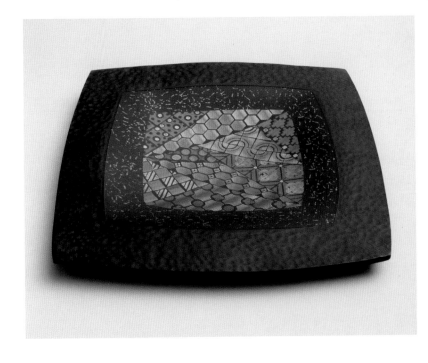

John Wheeldon Fellow

I have been making raku for around fifteen years, concentrating mainly on the copper matt surface. The combination of smoky black and rich colour still interests me. I have recently been investigating the possibility of combining terra sigillata surfaces with lustres, which are subsequently raku-fired. This makes reference to earlier work where I decorated black stoneware with lustres. Combining the two techniques suddenly made sense; I do not know why it took me so long. I decorate the new work with stamps, resists, smoke resists and lustres. I am excited by the new journey.

4 West End, Wirksworth, Derbyshire, DE4 4EG Tel 01629 822356
Email j.wheeldon@tiscali.co.uk Website www.johnwheeldonceramics.co.uk

Whichford Pottery

Jim and Dominique Keeling met at Cambridge in 1971 where Jim was studying archaeology and Dominique was reading English. They began making sgraffito earthenware soon after leaving university, but had a long pause while Jim set up his flowerpot pottery and Dominique had their family. They returned to glazed ware in 1995. The pots for glazing are thrown by Jim, their shapes inspired by Near Eastern and European traditions, then decorated by Dominique. Her designs are ever-varying and often feature mythology, domestic life, dance and the human figure.

Whichford Pottery, Whichford, Nr Shipston-on-Stour, Warwickshire, CV36 5PG
Tel 01608 684416 Email sgraffito@whichfordpottery.com
Opening hours Mon-Fri 9am-5pm, Sat & Bank Holidays 10am-4pm, Sun (Apr-Sept only) 11am-4pm

David White Fellow

My work is predominantly crackle-glazed porcelain. I have produced a wide range of glazes which craze in various ways. The glazes are blended by carefully controlled spraying, using up to five glazes on a pot. On cooling, the pots are coated with a carbon-based ink which is washed off immediately. By doing perpetual tests and experiments and making copious notes of how the pots were glazed, a degree of control over the crazing can be achieved. Almost fifty percent of each firing are considered unsatisfactory and are reglazed and refired.

4 Callis Court Road, Broadstairs, Kent, CT10 3AE Tel 01843 863145 Email didave@white-art.co.uk
Website www.theceramicartist.com Visitors welcome by appointment

Mary White Fellow

Trained at Newport School of Art,
Hammersmith School of Art and Goldsmiths
College, London (ATD). Initiated the
Typography Department and the Ceramic
Workshop in Atlantic College, St Donats
Castle, 1962-72, then set up own workshop in
Llantwit Major, Wales. Later moved to
Malmesbury, Wiltshire, and opened gallery
with husband artist Charles (deceased 1997).
In 1980 moved into wine-producing village in
south west Germany. Was awarded the State
Prize for Ceramic in 1982, then other prizes
internationally. I have exhibited all over
Europe and USA, and had work shown in the
Musée des Arts Decoratifs, Louvre, Paris. My
work is represented in many international col-
lections and museums and in numerous books
and magazines. I am also a professional callig-
rapher and integrate letters in clay forms.
Author of *Letters and Clay* (A&C Black, 2002).

Zimmerplatzweg 6, 55599 Wonsheim, Germany Tel +49 (0) 6703 2922
Fax +49 (0) 6703 305833 Email mary.white@t-online.de

Tony White

Established his present workshop at Cwmystwyth, Ceredigion, Wales, in 1990 and since then all his work has been fired using the raku method. He likes variety in his work, which includes throwing and extruding forms which are decorated in a semi-abstract manner. He also builds animal figures including Indian runner ducks, dogs, cats, puffins, penguins, chickens etc. His work is sold through gallery shops, exhibitions and ceramic fairs, and also by a visit to his home studio or through the website.

Upper Lodge, Hafod, Cymystwyth, Ystrad Meurig, Ceredigion, SY25 6DX Tel 01974 282202
Email tonyjohnwhite@btinternet.com Website www.tonywhiteceramics.co.uk

Caroline Whyman Fellow

Porcelain is a remarkable material, smooth, white and tricky to handle, posing many problems to the maker at every stage of its gestation. It is this challenge that keeps me working and evolving to probe into its mysteries and possibilities. For some years now I have explored the thrown form and developed the use of symbolic grids, influenced by and referencing the strong systematic geometry from early woven textiles of many cultures whilst incorporating the deeper meaning of a sacred symbolism that lies behind these patterns. I have real pleasure in designing forms that stand alone as individual pieces and yet have the possibility of another life in combination with flowers; the utility is not in the vessel but the space it contains.

21 Iliffe Yard, Crampton Street, London, SE17 3QA Mobile 07958 908450
Fax 020 7820 8207 Email whyman@dircon.co.uk Visitors by appointment

Jon Williams

I approach my throwing in a playful and experimental manner. When I sit at the wheel I may have a rough line drawing to work from, at other times I just enjoy seeing what the stuff can do. Freshly thrown pots are squashed, stretched, cut and assembled to produce an effect. I supplement my pot making with a busy programme of educational projects and recreational workshops. I have the space and equipment at my studio,

Eastnor Pottery, to accommodate up to twenty-five children or fifteen adults. Although I encourage individuals, groups and schools to work at the pottery, this is not always practical, therefore I regularly take my potter's wheel into businesses, schools and community settings to conduct workshops and participatory demonstrations.

Eastnor Pottery, Home Farm, Eastnor, Ledbury, Herefordshire, HR8 1RD Tel/Fax 01531 633886
Email eastnor.pottery@ukonline.co.uk Website www.eastnorpottery.co.uk or www.flyingpotter.com
Visitors welcome by appointment

Maggie Williams

I am interested in the dialogue between form, surface and space and I have been experimenting for some years with the balance and integration of these elements. Contrasts between tightly drawn silhouettes and loose, intricate surfaces have always been a focus of my work; fragility, light and shadow have, more recently, become important qualities. My ceramics is often vessel-based, although not usually very functional, and also includes some installation works. At present I am using porcelain; slip-cast and pierced or, with additions of paper, slip-trailed into moulds to create reticulated vessels which allow line and space to enclose volume, define form and create pattern. Studio based in Faversham since 1984. Subject leader for BA and MA Ceramics at Canterbury Christ Church University.

Poulders, 65 Ospringe Street, Ospringe, Faversham, Kent, ME13 8TW Tel 01795 531768
Email mw2@canterbury.ac.uk Visitors welcome by appointment

Peter Wills

After thirty years' involvement in ceramics,
half as a professional potter, one occasionally
gets referred to as an expert. I think we all
know that even after a lifetime's study anyone
will only have scratched the surface of this
subject; one that continues to inspire, tanta-
lise, amaze and frustrate. Most current work is
porcelain made with blends of various English
and French Limoges porcelain, raw-glazed and
oxidised, fired to cone 9 flat; approx. 1290°C.

Home: 44 Newcastle Hill, Bridgend, South Wales, CF31 4EY **Tel** 01656 662902 **Mobile** 07790 100183
Studio/Gallery: 8 Park Street, Bridgend, CF31 4AU **Email** peter@peterwills.co.uk **Website** www.peterwills.co.uk
Visitors to studio welcome by appointment: Mon-Fri 10am-5.30pm, Sat 10am-2pm; other times by arrangement

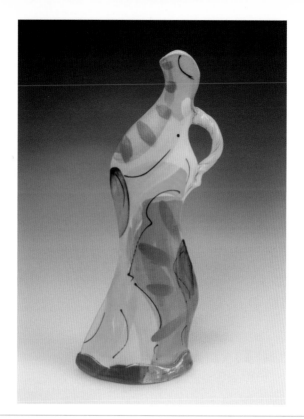

Richard Wilson

After training in Norwich with Roger Ledieu in the early 1970s, I became a journeyman potter, travelling and working with many craftsmen in Australia, New Zealand, Germany and England before setting up my present workshop in Dorset. My slipware pots have been mostly functional with more recent sculptural forms, all brightly decorated in loose abstract patterns using brushes and sliptrailer on terracotta clay.

They are fired in a gas kiln to 1120°C. I sell throughout the UK and in Puerto Rico. I am a former chairman of the West Country Potters Association and a member of the Somerset Guild.

Chapel Yard Pottery, Abbotsbury, Weymouth, Dorset, DT3 4JR Email lwilson@toucansurf.com
Website www.chapelyard.co.uk Workshop open to the public: Tues-Sat 9am-5pm

David Winckley Fellow

Born in Lancashire in 1939. Trained initially as a painter at the School of Fine Art, Reading University and at Pembroke College, Cambridge. Began making pots with the late Bernard Forrester at Dartington in 1963 and opened his first workshop in Bristol the following year. Since 1966 he has been at his present workshop in West Somerset. Makes hand-thrown stoneware and porcelain with a singular commitment to pots for daily use.

Some individual pieces, but the main production is an exceptionally wide range of pots for oven, kitchen and table. Firings are in a 230 cubic foot two-chamber oil-fired kiln.

Somerset

Vellow Pottery, Lower Vellow, Williton, Taunton, Somerset, TA4 4LS Tel 01984 656458
Workshop and pottery shop open Mon-Sat 8.30am-6pm

Tessa Wolfe Murray

Trained at Goldsmiths College (1982-4). My studio in Hove is situated in a cobbled mews close to the sea. I work alongside other ceramists and furniture designers. Smoke firing still plays an important role in my work but more recent slab-built vases are decorated only with an interplay of incised glaze lines. The dynamic of space in between a group of pots is also a developing theme. I use earthenware and earthstone clays, fired twice in an electric kiln to 1120°C. Slips and glazes form the decoration and when used, smoke firing is quick and controlled, a method I developed to suit ware that is glazed internally. I sell my work through craft and fine art galleries, ceramic fairs and directly from the studio.

Wolfe Murray

Biscuit Studio, 12B Wilbury Grove, Hove, East Sussex, BN3 3JQ Tel 01273 720625
Email tessa@wolfemurrayceramics.co.uk Website www.wolfemurrayceramics.co.uk Visitors welcome by appointment

Mary Wondrausch Honorary Fellow

I work in earthenware using a honey glaze for the more traditional slip-trailed pots. I specialise in individually commissioned commemorative plates, which customers are able to collect from the workshop, converted from an eighteenth-century stable in a magical setting. These can also be posted worldwide. The subject of my gouache paintings is often reflected in the central decoration of the large cheese platters. Latterly I have been developing a more painterly style with a quince tree motif (above) using slips as well as oxides. My work is predominantly functional, reflecting my interest in food.

The Pottery, Brickfields, Compton, Nr Guildford, Surrey, GU3 1HZ Tel 01483 414097
Opening hours: Mon-Fri 10am-1pm, 2-4pm; Sat-Sun 2-4pm; please telephone first

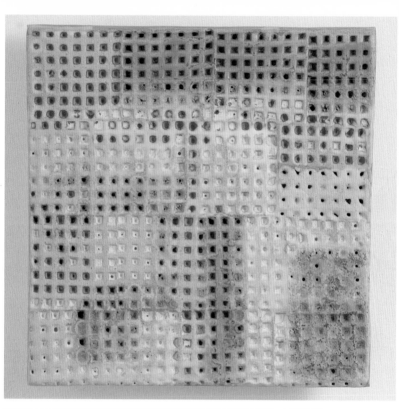

Gary Wood Fellow

Pots and wall pieces in stoneware. A large
selection of Gary Wood's work can be seen,
by appointment, at his gallery in Bristol.
(Photo: Jason Ingram)

Gary Wood

One Two Five, Box Road, Bath, BA1 7LR Tel/Fax 01225 858888
Email garywood@theceramicartist.com

Philip Wood

After fifteen years in the neighbouring village of Nunney, Philip Wood moved to his new studio in Whatley in 2004. He continues to make his sprigged earthenware, recognisable by its soft washed exterior, creamy glaze and precise detailing. He makes all manner of tableware.

Linden Mead Studio, Whatley, Nr Frome, Somerset, BA11 3JX Tel 01373 836425
Email philipwood1@gmail.com Visitors welcome by appointment

Rachel Wood

I trained in ceramics at Loughborough College of Art and graduated in 1999. Shortly afterwards I set up my workshop in my home in Mansfield. I throw, assemble and manipulate my pots using stoneware clay. Integral to each stage of the making process is adding my personal sensitive touch on the surface of the pots – a dent in the soft clay, a tear, rip, and a finger or handprint in the glaze. The natural sponta-neous qualities of the clay are what are important to me, so that each pot conveys its own spirit and character. My fingerprints alone serve as my potter's mark.

11 Murray Street, Mansfield, Nottinghamshire, NG18 4AR
Tel 01623 642425 Email rachel.wood1@tiscali.co.uk

Steve Woodhead Fellow

My current work is a mixture of both thrown
and handbuilt forms, using both stoneware
and porcelain clays. The work is decorated
with a range of coloured glazes that flow
and tumble over the textured forms. I have
always been fascinated by the teapot form
and recently have been making a variety of
individual teapots. Author of *The Teapot
Book* (A&C Black).

65 Shakespeare Gardens, Rugby, Warwickshire, CV22 6HA Tel 01788 522178
Website and email via www.teapotbook.com Visitors welcome by appointment

Gill Wright

Gill Wright works in white earthenware,
making handbuilt pots, part-glazed and
part-burnished.

52 South Street, Epsom, Surrey, KT18 7PQ Tel 01372 723908
Workshop in Headley. Visitors welcome by appointment

The Ceramics Book | 284

Takeshi Yasuda Fellow

Takeshi Yasuda trained at Daisei Pottery in
Mashiko, Japan (1963-65). Worked in UK
since 1973. Exhibits widely and has work
in public and private collections abroad
and in the UK, including the Victoria and
Albert Museum. Currently director of the
pottery workshop and sculpture factory in
Jingdezhen and tutor at the Royal College
of Art, London.

Garden Flat, 14 Grosvenor Place, Bath BA1 6AX Tel 01225 334136 (Home) or 01225 313492 (Studio)
Mobile 07815 068146 Email t.yasuda@btinternet.com

Alistair Young

Alistair Young established his first studio in Gloucestershire in 1978 producing thrown domestic stoneware. He has developed studio ceramics courses at the Royal Forest of Dean College, is the author of *Setting Up a Pottery Workshop* (A&C Black, 1999) and has also worked on projects with Royal Doulton and Asprey, designing and making limited edition salt-glazed pieces. Alistair's pots range from large decorated plates to smaller items of a functional nature. The forms are thrown and often altered by pressing and denting and applying porcelain details. The saltglaze firing enhances the texture and colour of the clay body and softens the smooth glazes of the interiors.

Guy Hall Cottage, Awre, Newnham-on-Severn, Gloucestershire, GL14 1EL Tel 01594 510343
Email email@alistairyoung.co.uk Website www.alistairyoung.co.uk Visitors welcome by appointment

Paul Young

My workshop is on the platform of a Victorian train station. This is now home to the Shakerstone Railway Society and the preserved battlefield line, with steam and diesel engines passing the door, and in close proximity to the famous Bosworth battlefield of 1485. Here I produce a range of domestic and decorative earthenware with slip-trailed decoration. The work is thrown on a kick-wheel or handbuilt, very often combining both techniques. Using coloured slips and glazes, it is fired in a downdraught wood or electric kiln.

Station Pottery, Shenton Station, Shenton, Nr Nuneaton, Warwickshire, CV13 0AA Mobile 07711 628337
Email potterpaulyoung@hotmail.com Workshop open most weekends, advisable to telephone first

Addresses

1 Adrian Abberley Fellow
95A Sheen Road, Richmond-upon-Thames,
Surrey, TW9 1YJ
Tel 020 8948 1234
Please telephone for enquiries

2 Billy Adams Fellow
4 Allensbank Road, Heath, Cardiff, CF14 3RB
Tel 07876 451887
Email adamsfamily@ceramicscardiff.freeserve.co.uk

3 David Allnatt
3 Poplar Gardens, Napton on the Hill,
Warwickshire, CV47 8PG
Tel 01926 813438 Website www.allnattceramics.com

4 Marilyn Andreetti
Mud Sweat and Tears Studio Pottery, Belle Vue,
16 Gews Corner, Cheshunt, Hertfordshire, EN8 9BX
Tel 01992 639969 Fax 01992 637258
Email mandreetti@hotmail.co.uk

5 Tim Andrews Fellow
Woodbury Studio/Gallery, Greenway,
Woodbury, Exeter, EX5 1LW
Tel/Fax 01395 233475
Email timandrews@eclipse.co.uk
Website www.timandrewsceramics.co.uk
Open Mon-Fri 10am-6pm, Sat 10am-1pm but please ring
out of season. Open daily 10am-6pm during exhibitions

6 Arabella Gail Ark
UK: 38 Cater Gardens, Guildford, Surrey, GU3 3BY
Tel 01483 306820
Hawaii: 45-575 Hana Hwy, Hana, Maui, Hawaii 96713
Tel +1 808 248 4890
Email arabella@arkceramics.net
Website www.arkceramics.net
Visitors welcome to Hawaii studio by appointment

7 Mick Arnup Fellow
Arnup Studios and Gallery, Holtby, York, YO19 5UA
Tel 01904 489377
Visitors welcome by appointment

8 Keith Ashley Fellow
The Chocolate Factory, Farleigh Place, London, N16 7SX
Tel/Fax 020 7503 7896
Visitors welcome by appointment

9 Jacqui Atkin Fellow
White Cottage, 3 Glyn Morlas,
St Martins, Oswestry, SY11 3EE
Tel 01691 773670 Email j.p.atkin@btopenworld.com
Visitors are very welcome but please telephone first –
you will need directions.

10 Felicity Aylieff Fellow
Garden Flat, 14 Grosvenor Place, Bath BA1 6AX
Tel 01225 334136 (Home) or 01225 313492 (Studio)
Mobile 07714 212124 Email aylieff@btinternet.com or
felicity.aylieff@rca.ac.uk

11 Elizabeth Aylmer
Buzon 911, 11690 Olvera, Cadiz, Spain
Tel +34 956 234060 Mobile +34 677 099086
Visitors welcome by appointment

12 Duncan Ayscough Fellow
Farmers, Bethlehem, Carmarthenshire, SA19 9DU
Email duncan@ayscoughceramics.co.uk or
dayscough@uwic.ac.uk
Website www.ayscoughceramics.co.uk or
www.cardiffceramics.com

13 Sylph Baier
3 Florence Road, Brighton, BN1 6DL
Tel/Fax 01273 540552
Email sylphbaier@sylph.fslife.co.uk
Website www.sylph.fslife.co.uk
Visitors welcome by appointment

14 Chris Barnes
The Chocolate Factory, Farleigh Place,
Stoke Newington, London, N16 7SX
Tel 020 7503 6961 (Studio)
Mobile 07719 454198
Email cb_1959@blueyonder.co.uk
Website www.buy-design.co.uk
Visitors welcome by appointment

15 Richard Baxter
Old Leigh Studios, 61 High Street,
Old Town, Leigh-on-Sea, Essex, SS9 2EP
Tel 01702 470490
Email richard@richardbaxter.com
Website www.richardbaxter.com
Open Tues-Sun 11am-5pm; closed Mon

16 Deborah Baynes
Nether Hall, Shotley, Ipswich, Suffolk, IP9 1PW
Tel 01473 788300 Fax 01473 787055
Email deb@deborahbaynes.co.uk
Website www.potterycourses.net
Visitors welcome by appointment

17 Peter Beard Fellow
Tanners Cottage, Welsh Road, Cubbington,
Leamington Spa, Warwickshire, CV32 7UB
Tel 01926 428481 Email peter@peterbeard.co.uk
Website www.peterbeard.co.uk

18 Jan Beeny
Home: 8 Grenville Road, Penylan, Cardiff, CF23 5BP
Studio: 54B Bute Street, Cardiff Bay, Cardiff, CF10 5AF
Tel 029 2025 8060
Email janbeeny@hotmail.com
Visitors by appointment only

19 Jonna Behrens
Gardens Cottage, Culham Court,
Henley on Thames, Oxfordshire, RG9 3DN
Tel 01491 575433 Email jonna@behrens.demon.co.uk
Visitors welcome by appointment

20 Beverly Bell-Hughes Fellow
Fron Dirion, Conwy Road,
Llandudno Junction, Conwy, LL31 9AY
Tel 01492 572575
Visitors welcome by appointment

21 Terry Bell-Hughes Fellow
Fron Dirion, Conwy Road, Llandudno Junction,
Conwy, LL31 9AY Tel 01492 572575
Visitors welcome by appointment

22 Julian Belmonte
4 Butts Road, Alton, Hampshire, GU34 1NE
Tel 01420 542353 Email mail@julianbelmonte.co.uk
Website www.julianbelmonte.co.uk
White earthenware focusing on simplicity of form,
scale and balance. Visitors welcome by appointment

23 Kochevet Bendavid Fellow
147 Overhill Road, East Dulwich, London, SE22 0PT
Tel/Fax 020 8516 1241
Email kookiebendavid@hotmail.co.uk
Visitors welcome by appointment

24 Maggie Angus Berkowitz Fellow
21-23 Park Road, Milnthorpe, Cumbria, LA7 7AD
Tel/Fax 01539 563970
Email maggie@maggieberkowitz.co.uk
Website www.maggieberkowitz.co.uk

25 John Berry Fellow
45 Chancery Lane, Beckenham, Kent, BR3 6NR
Tel 020 8658 0351

26 Rob Bibby
Woodnewton Pottery, 43 Main Street, Woodnewton,
Oundle, East Northamptonshire, PE8 5EB
Tel 01780 470866
Visitors welcome by appointment

27 David Binns Fellow
Ty Tal, 34 Park Street, Denbigh, Denbighshire,
North Wales, LL16 3DB
Tel 01745 814441
Email dsbinns@hotmail.com
Website www.davidbinnsceramics.com
Visitors welcome by appointment

28 Matthew Blakely
9 Abbey Lane, Lode, Cambridgeshire, CB5 9EP
Tel 01223 811959
Email smashingpots@uk2.net
Website www.matthewblakely.co.uk
Visitors welcome by appointment

29 Gill Bliss
Mobile 07751 367076 Email gillbliss@btinternet.com
Website www.gillbliss.com

30 David Body
John O'Groats Pottery, 3 The Craft Centre, John
O'Groats, Wick, Caithness KW1 4YR
Tel/Fax 01955 611284
Email info@jogpot.co.uk Website www.jogpot.co.uk
Open Apr-Sept: daily 9.30am-5.30pm, except Sunday
12.30am-5.30pm. Oct-Mar: Tues-Sat 9.30am-5pm
Visitors welcome by appointment

31 Martin Booth
49 Heaton Terrace, Porthill,
Newcastle-under-Lyme, Staffordshire, ST5 8PJ
Tel 01782 639182
Visitors welcome by appointment

32 Richard Boswell
66 Wallington Shore Road,
Fareham, Hampshire, PO16 8SJ
Tel 01329 511497
Email richatwallington@yahoo.co.uk
Visitors welcome by appointment

33 Joy Bosworth Fellow
22A Worcester Road, Hagley, West Midlands, DY9 OLD
Tel 01562 884810 Email info@joybosworthceramics.com

34 Charles Bound
Street Farm, Geufford, Welshpool, Powys, SY21 9DR
Tel 01938 590230
Email joy@geuffordd.fsnet.co.uk
Visitors welcome by appointment

35 Clive Bowen Fellow
Shebbear Pottery, Shebbear, Beaworthy, Devon, EX21 5QZ
Tel 01409 281271
Wholesale and retail customers are
welcome at the showroom

36 Sheila Boyce
36 Gwendolin Avenue, Birstall, Leicester, LE4 4HD
Tel 0116 220 7105 Email oncefired@aol.com
Website www.oncefired.co.uk
Visitors welcome by appointment

37 Loretta Braganza Fellow
The Coach House, 198 Mount Vale, York, YO24 1DL
Tel 01904 630454
Email loretta@braganzas.freeserve.co.uk
Visitors welcome by appointment

38 Chris Bramble
110-116 Kingsgate Road, London, NW6 2JG
Tel 020 7419 7260 Email chrisbramble@yahoo.com
Thrown and figurative ware, influenced by Rodin and
African craftmanship. Open 9am-5pm, but please
telephone first

39 Benedict Brierley
25 Turner Avenue, Loughborough,
Leicestershire, LE11 2DA
Tel 01509 828349 Email benedict@supanet.com
Visitors welcome by appointment

40 Carlo Briscoe and Edward Dunn Fellows
Gwaith Menyn, Llanglydwen, Carmarthenshire, SA34 0XP
Tel/Fax 01994 419402
Visitors welcome by appointment

41 David Brown
DB Pottery, Church Street, Merriott, Somerset, TA16 5PR
Tel 01460 75655
Showroom open most days but advisable to phone first

42 Melanie Brown
Garden Cottage, Coldbrook, Abergavenny,
Monmouthshire, NP7 9ST
Tel 01873 858015 Email mel@artwks.co.uk
Visitors welcome by appointment

43 Sandy Brown Fellow
3 Marine Parade, Appledore, Bideford, Devon, EX39 1PJ
Tel 01237 478219
Email sandy@sandybrown.freeserve.co.uk
Website www.sandybrownarts.com

44 Susan Bruce
4 Pinewood, Woodbridge, Suffolk, IP12 4DS
Tel 01394 384865
Email susanbruce@ceramics33.freeserve.co.uk

45 Victoria Bryan
Fig Tree House, 19 Northdown Avenue, Cliftonville,
Margate, Kent, CT9 2NL
Mobile 07973 898473 Fax 01843 297919
No showroom; visitors welcome by appointment

46 Vanessa Bullick
Crauford, Kevock Road, Lasswade,
Mid Lothian, EH18 1HX
Tel 0131 229 9553 Mobile 07768 493225

47 Karen Bunting
53 Beck Road, London, E8 4RE
Tel 020 7249 3016 Email bunting.all@virgin.net
Visitors welcome by appointment

48 Jan Bunyan
4 Bridge Road, Butlers Marston, Warwick, CV35 0ND
Tel 01926 641560
Email janbunyan@butlersmarston.fsnet.co.uk
Visitors welcome by appointment

49 Deirdre Burnett Fellow
48 Gipsy Hill, London, SE19 1NL
Tel 020 8670 6565
Email deirdreburnett@btinternet.com
Visitors welcome by appointment

50 Ian Byers Fellow
16 Stroud Road, London, SE25 5DR
Tel 020 8654 0225
Email ianbyersceramics@hotmail.com

51 John Calver Fellow
23 Silverdale Road, Yealand Redmayne,
Carnforth, Lancashire, LA5 9TA
Tel 01524 781362 Email calver@freenet.co.uk
Visitors are welcome at the workshop but unusual
working hours makes telephoning first advisable

52 Kyra Cane Fellow
5 West Workshops, Harley Foundation, Welbeck,
Worksop, Nottinghamshire, S80 3LW
Tel 01909 489555 Email kc-jb@ntlworld.com

53 Daphne Carnegy Fellow
Kingsgate Workshops,
110-116 Kingsgate Road, London, NW6 2JG
Tel 020 7328 2051 or 020 8442 0337
Email d.carnegy@tiscali.co.uk
Visitors welcome by appointment

54 Simon Carroll
Unit 4C, The Airfield, St Merryn,
Padstow, Cornwall, PL28 8PU
Tel 01841 520072 Website www.simoncarroll.co.uk
Visitors welcome by appointment

55 Sheila Casson Honorary Fellow
Wobage Farm, Upton Bishop, Ross-on-Wye,
Herefordshire, HR9 7QP Tel 01989 780233
Fax 01989 780495 Wobage Makers Gallery open
Apr-Sept: Thurs-Sun 10am-5pm; Oct-Mar: Sat-Sun only;
other times by appointment only

56 Trevor Chaplin
Marridge Hill Cottage, Ramsbury,
Marlborough, Wiltshire, SN8 2HG
Tel 01672 520486
Visitors welcome by appointment

57 Linda Chew Fellow
42 Cheriton Road, Winchester, Hampshire, SO22 5AY
Tel 01962 867218 Email chewceramics@yahoo.com
Work can be viewed at www.ruffordceramiccentre.org.uk
www.southernceramicgroup.co.uk
www.bluestonegallery.com
Visitors welcome by appointment

58 Bruce Chivers
The School House, Dunsford, Exeter, Devon, EX6 7DD
Tel 01647 252099 Email brucechivers@talk21.com
Website www.brucechivers.co.uk
Visitors welcome by appointment

59 Kevin de Choisy Fellow
50 Bove Town, Glastonbury, Somerset, BA6 8JE
Tel 01458 835055
Email glazedandconfused@tiscali.co.uk
Visitors welcome by appointment

60 Derek Clarkson Honorary Fellow
The Poplars, Bacup, Lancashire, OL13 8AD
Tel 01706 874541
Visitors welcome by appointment

61 Peter Clough Fellow
8 Southville Terrace, Harrogate,
North Yorkshire, HG1 3HH
Tel 01423 567716 Mobile 07787 521089
Email potclough@hotmail.com
Website www.peterclough.com
Visitors welcome by appointment

62 Russell Coates Fellow
The Haven, Gare Hill Road, Witham Friary,
Frome, Somerset, BA11 5EX
Tel 01373 836171 Mobile 07745 477135
Visitors welcome by appointment

63 Rosemary Cochrane
76 Mill Street, Usk, Monmouthshire, NP15 1AW
Tel 01291 671567 Mobile 07968 370986
Email rosemary@p-y-s.freeserve.co.uk

64 Roger Cockram Fellow

Chittlehampton Pottery and Gallery, Chittlehampton,
North Devon, EX37 9PX
Tel 01769 540420
Email roger@rogercockram-ceramics.co.uk
Website www.rogercockram-ceramics.co.uk
Open Mon-Fri 10am-1pm, 2-5.30pm; also often open at
weekends or by request; telephone first

65 Elaine Coles

Chobham Pottery, 73A High Street,
Chobham, Surrey, GU24 8AF
Tel 01276 856769
Email pottery@ecoles.go-plus.net
Website www.elainecoles.co.uk
Visitors welcome by appointment

66 Nic Collins Fellow

The Barn Pottery, North Bovey Road,
Moretonhampstead, Devon, TQ13 8PQ
Tel 01647 441198
Email nic.collins4@btopenworld.com
Visitors welcome by appointment

67 Jennifer Colquitt

Field Ceramics, Holloway Chambers, 27 Priory Street,
Dudley, West Midlands, DY1 1HA
Tel 01384 455591
Visitors welcome by appointment

68 Jo Connell

Witherley Lodge, 12 Watling Street, Witherley,
Atherstone, Warwickshire, CV9 1RD
Tel 01827 712128 Email jo@jjconnell.co.uk
Website www.jjconnell.co.uk
Visitors welcome by appointment

69 Clare Conrad

29 Westcourt Lane, Shepherdswell,
Nr Dover, Kent, CT15 7PT
Tel/Fax 01304 831019
Email clareconrad@hotmail.com

70 David Constantine White

Briar Hey Pottery, Burnley Road, Mytholmroyd,
West Yorkshire, HX7 5PF
Tel/Fax 01422 885725
Open usual trading hours

71 Sophie Cook

Cockpit Arts, Studio 109,18-22 Creekside,
Deptford, London, SE8 3DZ
Tel 020 8694 8363
Website www.sophiecook.com
Visitors welcome by appointment. Seconds sale
twice a year

72 Delan Cookson Fellow

3 King George Memorial Walk, Phillack,
Hayle, Cornwall, TR27 5AA
Tel 01736 755254 Email delancookson@hotmail.com
Visitors welcome by appointment

73 Emmanuel Cooper Fellow

Fonthill Pottery, 38 Chalcot Road, London, NW1 8LP
Tel 020 7722 9090 Mobile 07973 816407
Email emmanuelcooper@lineone.net
Visitors welcome by appointment

74 Prue Cooper

Studio 213E, Wandsworth Business Village,
Broomhill Road, London, SW18 4JQ
Tel 020 8871 5118 Email info@pruecooper.co.uk
Website www.pruecooper.co.uk
Visitors welcome by appointment

75 Gilles Le Corre Fellow

19 Howard Street, Oxford, OX4 3AY
Tel 01865 245289
Email elaine@lecorre5.wanadoo.co.uk
Visitors welcome by appointment

76 Jane Cox

85 Wickham Road, Brockley, London, SE4 1NH
Tel/Fax 020 8692 6742
Email jane@janecoxceramics.com
Website www.janecoxceramics.com
Visitors welcome by appointment

77 Jan Crombie

37 St Mary's Road, Oxford, OX4 1PY
Tel 01865 722429 Fax 01865 432642
Visitors welcome by appointment

78 Molly Curley

32 South Rise, Llanishen, Cardiff, CF14 0RH
Tel/Fax 029 2075 6428 Email mollydcurley@tiscali.co.uk
Visitors welcome by appointment

79 Eddie Curtis
Middle Rigg, Wearhead, Bishop Auckland,
County Durham, DL13 1HS
Tel 01388 537379 Website www.eddiecurtis.co.uk

80 Margaret Curtis
Middle Rigg, Wearhead, Bishop Auckland,
County Durham, DL13 1HS
Tel 01388 537379 Website www.eddiecurtis.co.uk

81 Sylvia Dales
75/77 Melford Road, Sudbury, Suffolk, CO10 1JT
Tel 01787 374581 or 01787 378434
Email pots@sylviedales.fslife.co.uk
Visitors welcome

82 Louise Darby
Clay Barn, Redhill, Alcester, Warwickshire, B49 6NQ
Tel 01789 765214
Email louise.darby@btopenworld.com

83 Dartington Pottery Fellow
Shinners Bridge, Dartington, Totnes, Devon, TQ9 6JE
Tel 01803 864163 Fax 01803 864641
Email enquiries@dartingtonpottery.co.uk
Website www.dartingtonpottery.co.uk
Shop opening hours: Mon-Sat 10am-6pm

84 Patia Davis
Wobage Farm, Upton Bishop, Ross-on-Wye,
Herefordshire, HR9 7QP
Tel/Fax 01989 780495
Wobage Makers Gallery open Apr-Sept: Thurs-Sun
10am-5pm; Oct-Mar: Sat-Sun only; other times by
appointment only

85 Joyce Davison
Ranters, 75 Pales Green, Castle Acre, Norfolk, PE32 2AL
Tel 01760 755405
Email joycedavison.ranters@virgin.net
Visitors welcome by appointment

86 John Dawson
47 Heathwood Gardens, Charlton, London, SE7 8ES
Tel 020 8316 1919 Email john16749@btinternet.com
Website www.btinternet.com/~john16749
Visitors welcome by appointment

87 Richard Dewar Fellow
Keryavec, 56550 Locoal-Mendon, France
Email dewar.ceramics@wanadoo.fr
Website perso.wanadoo.fr/dewar.ceramics

88 Peter and Jill Dick Fellows
Coxwold Pottery, Coxwold, York, YO61 4AA
Tel 01347 868344 Email info@coxwoldpottery.co.uk
Website www.coxwoldpottery.co.uk
Visitors welcome to the showroom and pottery garden
by appointment

89 Susan Disley
Studio 3, Tan Gallop, Welbeck, Nottingham, S80 3LW
Tel/Fax 01909 488989
Website www.susandisley.co.uk

90 Mike Dodd Fellow
The Pottery, Dove Workshops, Barton Road, Butleigh,
Glastonbury, Somerset, BA6 8TL Tel/Fax 01458 850385
Email mdodd@clara.co.uk Website www.mikedodd.info
Visitors welcome by appointment

91 Rosalie Dodds
14 Rugby Road, Brighton, BN1 6EB
Tel 01273 501743

92 Jack Doherty Fellow
Hooks Cottage, Lea Bailey, Ross-on-Wye,
Herefordshire, HR9 5TY
Tel/Fax 01989 750644
Email jack.doherty@virgin.net
Website www.dohertyporcelain.com
Visitors welcome at the workshop and showroom
by appointment

93 Karen Downing
Richmond House, Gedgrave, Orford, Suffolk, IP12 2BU
Tel/Fax 01394 450313
Email karen.downing@virgin.net
Visitors welcome by appointment

94 Bridget Drakeford
Upper Buckenhill Farmhouse, Fownhope,
Herefordshire, HR1 4PU
Tel 01432 860411
Email bdrakeford@bdporcelain.co.uk
Website www.bdporcelain.co.uk
Visitors welcome by appointment

95 Georgina Dunkley
The Chocolate Factory, Farleigh Place, London, N16 7SX
Tel 020 7690 8500
Email email@georginadunkley.com
Website www.georginadunkley.com
Visitors welcome by appointment

96 Sarah Dunstan
Gaolyard Studios, Dove Street,
St Ives, Cornwall, TR26 2LZ
Tel 01736 799336 or 01736 798928 (Evening)
Email sarahdunstanceramics@hotmail.com
Website www.sarahdunstan.co.uk
Visitors welcome by appointment

97 Phyllis Dupuy
48 Drayton Gardens, London, SW10 9SA
Tel 020 7373 4903   Email phyllisdupuy@yahoo.co.uk
Website www.phyllisdupuy.co.uk

98 Geoffrey Eastop Fellow
The Old Post Office, Ecchinswell,
Newbury, Berkshire, RG20 4TT
Tel 01635 298220   Email geastop@waitrose.com
Website www.bsgart.com

99 Sandra Eastwood
The Bungalow, 34 Hampton Road, Teddington, TW11 0JW
Tel 020 8286 4327
Email sandraeastwood@blueyonder.co.uk
Website www.studiopottery.co.uk
Workshop not open to the public. Trade enquiries
welcome

100 Victoria and Michael Eden Fellows
Parkside, Hale, Milnthorpe, Cumbria, LA7 7BL
Tel 01539 562342   Email mike@edenceramics.co.uk
Website www.edenceramics.co.uk
Visitors welcome, opening times normally Mon-Sat 11am-
5pm but please telephone first; see website for details

101 Libby Edmondson
Quaggs House Farm, Levens, Kendal, Cumbria, LA8 8PA
Tel 01539 561546   Email nigel.libby@uk4free.net
Website www.nigelandlibbyceramics.co.uk
Visitors welcome by appointment

102 Nigel Edmondson
Quaggs House Farm, Levens, Kendal, Cumbria, LA8 8PA
Tel 01539 561546   Email nigel.libby@uk4free.net
Website www.nigelandlibbyceramics.co.uk
Visitors welcome by appointment

103 Ross Emerson
Old Trickey's Farm House, Blackborough,
Cullompton, Devon, EX15 2HZ
Email rossemerson@talktalk.net
Website www.rossemerson.co.uk

104 Kirsti Buhler Fattorini
5 Broadway, Hale, Cheshire, WA15 0PF
Tel 0161 980 4504   Website www.kirstifattorini.com
Visitors welcome by appointment

105 Helen Felcey
12 Hoplea Street, Withington, Manchester M20 3FD
Mobile 07968 888696   Email helen@helenfelcey.co.uk
Website www.helenfelcey.co.uk
Helen Felcey produces a series of handmade ceramic
objects for use and display within the home. Pieces
are slip-cast in bone china, unglazed and polished to
a silk finish

106 Sotis Filippides
Studio IV8, Cooper House, 2 Michael Road,
London, SW6 2AD
Tel 020 7582 0980   Mobile 07733 151276
Email sotis@sotis.co.uk   Website www.sotis.co.uk

107 Ray Finch Honorary Fellow
Winchcombe Pottery, Broadway Road, Winchcombe,
Cheltenham, Gloucestershire, GL54 5NU
Tel 01242 602462
Email mike@winchcombepottery.co.uk
Website www.winchcombepottery.co.uk

108 Judith Fisher
Huntswood, St Helena's Lane, Streat,
Nr Hassocks, Sussex, BN6 8SD
Tel 01273 890088
Visitors welcome by appointment

109 Robert Fournier Fellow
8 Ladywood, Market Lavington, Devizes,
Wiltshire, SN10 4DL
Tel 01380 812342
Built Ducketts Wood Pottery, Hertfordshire 1946 – slip-
ware, tin glaze over slip, mosaics etc. With Sheila
Fournier – potting in London, at Castle Hill, Kent and
Lacock, Wiltshire, making stoneware and porcelain.
Many slides, films, books and until 1987 the Craft
Potters Association Archives. Retired from potting the
same year, continued with books including, in conjunc-
tion with Eric Yates-Owen, *British Studio Potters' Marks*,
published in 1999, second edition 2005

110 Penny Fowler
84 Middleton Road, Hackney, London, E8 4LN
Tel 020 7254 2707
Email penny.fowler@macunlimited.net
Visitors welcome by appointment

111 Alan Foxley
26 Shepherds Way, Saffron Walden, Essex, CB10 2AH
Tel 01799 522631 Email foxleyalan1@waitrose.com
Website www.studiopottery.co.uk
Visitors welcome by appointment

112 David Frith Fellow
Brookhouse Pottery, Brookhouse Lane,
Denbigh, Denbighshire, LL16 4RE
Tel/Fax 01745 812805
Email frith@brookhousepottery.co.uk
Website www.brookhousepottery.co.uk

113 Margaret Frith Fellow
Brookhouse Pottery, Brookhouse Lane, Denbigh,
Denbighshire, LL16 4RE
Tel/Fax 01745 812805
Email frith@brookhousepottery.co.uk
Website www.brookhousepottery.co.uk

114 Tessa Fuchs Fellow
Trinity Cottage, Chediston,
Halesworth, Suffolk, IP19 0AT
Tel 01986 875724
Visitors welcome by appointment

115 Liz Gale Fellow
Taplands Farm Cottage, Webbs Green, Soberton,
Southampton, Hampshire, SO32 3PY
Tel 023 9263 2686 Email lizgale@interalpha.co.uk
Visitors welcome by appointment

116 Tony Gant Fellow
53 Southdean Gardens, Southfields, London, SW19 6NT
Tel 020 8789 4518
Open Mon-Sat 10am-5pm; please telephone first

117 Tim Gee
165 Grenville Road, Plymouth, Devon, PL4 9QD
Tel 01752 225120 Email tim@timgeeceramics.co.uk
Website www.timgeeceramics.co.uk
Workshop open by arrangement

118 Carolyn Genders Fellow
Oak Farm, Lewes Road, Danehill,
East Sussex, RH17 7HD
Tel 01825 790575
Email carolyn.genders@boltblue.com
Website www.carolyngenders.co.uk
Visitors welcome by appointment

119 Christine Gittens
The Old Bakehouse Studio and Gallery, 7A Swan Street,
Llantrisant, Mid Glamorgan, CF72 8ED
Tel 01443 225899 Email christinegittins@aol.com
Open Wed-Sat 11am-5pm, Sun 2-5pm
Please telephone first if making a special journey

120 Richard Godfrey Fellow
1 Battisborough Cross, Holbeton,
Nr Plymouth, Devon, PL8 1JT
Tel 01752 830457
Email rg@richardgodfreyceramics.co.uk
Website www.richardgodfreyceramics.co.uk
Visitors welcome

121 Christopher Green Fellow
PO Box 115, Westbury-on-Trym, Bristol, BS9 3ND
Tel 0117 950 0852
Email cguk@seegreen.com
Visitors welcome by appointment

122 Paul Green
17 Woodlands Crescent, Poundbury,
Dorchester, Dorset, DT1 3RQ
Tel 01305 261522 Email abbeypot@aol.com
Visitors welcome by appointment

123 Ian Gregory Fellow
The Studio, Crumble Cottage, Ansty,
Dorchester, Dorset, DT2 7PN
Tel/Fax 01258 880891
Email igreg891@aol.com or ian@ian-gregory.co.uk
Website www.ian-gregory.co.uk
Workshop and studio open 2-6pm weekdays,
9am-6pm weekends, or by arrangement

124 Dimitra Grivellis
Unit 6, Broadway Market Mews, London, E8 4TS
Tel 020 7249 5455
Email dimitragrivellis@yahoo.co.uk

125 Barry Guppy
154A Southbourne Overcliff Drive,
Bournemouth, Dorset, BH6 3NH
Tel 01202 425495 (Home) Tel 01590 624911 (Studio)
Mobile 07986 744850
Email barry.guppy@btinternet.com
Website www.barryguppy.co.uk

126 Jennifer Hall
Spring Gardens, Llanwrthwl,
Llandrindod Wells, Powys, LD1 6NU
Tel 01597 810119
Email jennythepotter@hotmail.com
Visitors welcome by appointment

127 Morgen Hall Fellow
Chapter Arts Centre, Market Road,
Canton, Cardiff, CF5 1QE
Tel 029 2031 1050 ext 219 or 029 2023 8716
Website www.morgenhall.co.uk
Visitors welcome by appointment

128 Janet Halligan
The Old School, Church Minshull, Nantwich,
Cheshire, CW5 6EA Tel 01270 522416
Email mikehalligan@beeb.net
Visitors welcome by appointment

129 Frank Hamer Honorary Fellow
Llwyn-On, Croes-yn-y-Pant,
Mamhilad, Pontypool, NP4 8RE
Tel 01495 785700
Visitors welcome by appointment

130 Mohamed Hamid
Star Gallery Pottery, Fisher Street,
Lewes, East Sussex, BN7 1YJ
Tel 01273 483295 Mobile 07843 287187
Email info@mohamedhamid-pottery.co.uk
Website www.mohamedhamid-pottery.co.uk

131 Jane Hamlyn Fellow
Millfield Pottery, Everton, Nr Doncaster,
South Yorkshire, DN10 5DD
Tel 01777 817723
Visitors welcome by appointment

132 Lisa Hammond Fellow
Maze Hill Pottery, The Old Ticket Office, Woodlands
Park Road, Greenwich, London, SE10 9XE
Tel/Fax 020 8293 0048
Email mazehill.pottery@virgin.net
Website www.mazehill-pottery.com
Visitors welcome by appointment; students with genuine
interest in soda glaze accepted for work placements

133 Ashraf Hanna Fellow
Pen-y-Daith, Chapel Lane, Keeston,
Haverfordwest, Pembrokeshire, SA62 6EH
Tel 01437 710774
Email ashrafhanna.ceramics@btinternet.com
Visitors welcome by appointment

134 Keiko Harada
Park Lea, 36 West Park Crescent,
Roundhay, Leeds, LS8 2EQ
Tel/Fax 0113 266 3462 Email keiko17@ntlworld.com
Visitors welcome by appointment

135 Rebecca Harvey
Mobile 07967 320717 Website www.rebeccaharvey.com

136 Caroline Harvie
Scotts Buildings, Castle Hill, Kintore,
Aberdeenshire, AB51 0TZ
Tel 01467 632583 Email caroline.harvie@virgin.net
Please telephone for up-to-date address details

137 Michael and Barbara Hawkins Fellows
Port Issac Pottery, The Old Chapel,
Roscarrock Hill, Port Issac, Cornwall, PL29 3RG
Tel/Fax 01208 880625 Open Apr-Oct: daily 10am-4pm;
Nov-Mar: Thurs-Sun only

138 Peter Hayes Fellow
2 Cleveland Bridge, Bath, BA1 5DH
Tel/Fax 01225 466215 Email phayesceramics@aol.com
Website www.peterhayes-ceramics.com
Visitors welcome by appointment

139 Andrew Hazelden
The Pottery, The Street, Aldermaston, Berkshire, RG7 4LW
Tel 0118 971 3359
Email andrew@haze004.freeserve.co.uk
Website www.studiopottery.co.uk

140 Regina Heinz Fellow
Home: 52 Culmstock Road, London, SW11 6LU
Tel/Fax 020 7738 0813
Studio: Studio 213E, Wandsworth Business Village,
Broomhill Road, London, SW18 4JQ
Tel 020 8871 5118 Email regina_heinz@ceramart.net
Website www.ceramart.net

141 Rick Henham
Home: 2B Chy-an-Hall, Gulval,
Penzance, Cornwall, TR18 3LY
Tel 01736 332377
Studio: Gaolyard Studios, Dove Street,
St Ives, Cornwall, TR26 2LZ
Mobile 07880 794544
Email info@rickhenham.com
Website www.rickhenham.com

142 André Hess Fellow
32 Seaman Close, Park Street,
St Albans, Hertfordshire, AL2 2NX
Tel 01727 874299
Email andre@earthwaterfire.demon.co.uk
Visitors welcome by appointment

143 Karin Hessenberg Fellow
72 Broomgrove Road, Sheffield, S10 2NA
Tel 0114 266 1610 Email mail@karinhessenberg.co.uk
Website www.karinhessenberg.co.uk
Visitors welcome by appointment

144 Elaine Hewitt
Summerhill Cottage, Summerhill Lane,
Frensham, Surrey, GU10 3EW
Tel/Fax 01252 793955
Visitors welcome by appointment

145 John Higgins Fellow
32 Seaman Close, Park Street, St Albans,
Hertfordshire, AL2 2NX
Tel 01727 874299 Email johnceramics@aol.com
Visitors welcome by appointment

146 Andrew Hill Fellow
Quarry Hill Cottage, Park Lane, Carleton in Craven, Nr
Skipton, North Yorkshire, BD23 3BH
Tel 01756 795787 Email andrew@hill25.fsworld.co.uk
Visitors welcome by appointment

147 Wendy Hoare
135 Billing Road, Northampton, NN1 5RR
Tel 01604 622880
Website www.studiopottery.co.uk
Visitors welcome by appointment

148 John Hobson
Home: 8 Grenville Road, Penylan, Cardiff, CF23 5BP
Studio: 54B Bute Street, Cardiff Bay, Cardiff, CF10 5AF
Tel 029 2025 8060 Email johnmhobson@hotmail.com
Visitors welcome by appointment

149 Terri Holman
Northcombe, Moretonhampstead Road,
Bovey Tracey, Devon, TQ13 9NH
Tel 01626 835578 Visitors welcome by appointment

150 Duncan Hooson
9 Birchington Road, Crouch End, London, N8 8HR
Tel/Fax 020 8342 9032
Email duncan.hooson@hoosonwest.demon.co.uk
Visitors welcome by appointment

151 Harry Horlock-Stringer Fellow
King William House, Lopen,
South Petherton, Somerset, TA13 5JU
Tel/Fax 01460 242135

152 Joan Hoverstadt
37 Heaton Road, Withington, Manchester, M20 4PU
Tel 0161 445 7578

153 Ashley Howard Fellow
3 Albion Road, Tunbridge Wells, Kent, TN1 2PB
Tel 01892 533158 Mobile 07970 424762
Email ashleyhoward@ukonline.co.uk
Website www.studiopottery.co.uk
Visitors welcome by appointment

154 Joanna Howells Fellow
2 Cwrt Isaf, Tythegston, Bridgend,
Mid-Glamorgan, CF32 0ND
Tel 01656 784021 or 01656 788731
Email studio@joannahowells.co.uk
Website www.joannahowells.co.uk
Visitors welcome by appointment

155 John Huggins Fellow
Ruardean Garden Pottery, Ruardean, Forest of Dean,
Gloucestershire, GL17 9TP
Tel 01594 543577
Website www.ruardeanpottery.com
Workshop usually open Tues-Sat 10am-4.30pm

156 Edward Hughes
The Stables, Isel Hall, Cockermouth, Cumbria, CA13 0QG
Tel/Fax 01900 825 557
Website www.edwardhughes.members.beeb.net
Visitors welcome by appointment

157 Simon Hulbert Fellow
Brook Street Pottery, Hay-on-Wye, Hereford, HR3 5BQ
Tel 01497 821070 Email info@hayclay.co.uk
Website www.hayclay.co.uk
Studio and gallery open throughout the year

158 Tim Hurn
Home Farm House, Bettiscombe,
Bridport, Dorset, DT6 5NU
Tel 01308 868171
Email timhurn@bettiscombe96.fsnet.co.uk
Workshop open by appointment

159 Peter Ilsley
Whilton Locks Pottery, Whilton Locks,
Daventry, Northamptonshire, NN11 2NH
Tel/Fax 01327 842886
Website www.studiopottery.co.uk
Visitors welcome by appointment

160 Claire Ireland
35 Clifden Road, Brentford, Middlesex, TW8 0PB
Tel 020 8568 9287
Email claireirelanduk@yahoo.co.uk
Visitors welcome by appointment

161 Alvin Irving
Lancaster Pottery, The Covered Yard,
11 King Street, Lancaster, LA1 1JN
Tel 01524 33270
Visitors welcome

162 Bernard Irwin
The Barn, South Downs, Chyenhal, Nr Drift,
Penzance, Cornwall, TR19 6AW
Tel 01736 731899 Email studio@bernardirwin.com
Website www.bernardirwin.com
Visitors welcome by appointment

163 Paul Jackson Fellow
Helland Bridge Pottery, Helland Bridge,
Bodmin, Cornwall, PL30 4QR
Tel 01208 75240 Fax 01208 78893
Email paul@paul-jackson.co.uk
Website www.paul-jackson.co.uk

164 Anne James Fellow
Ashleigh, Gloucester Street, Painswick,
Gloucester, GL6 6QN
Tel 01452 813378 Email annejames@sjld.co.uk
Visitors welcome by appointment

165 Victoria Jardine
Archway Ceramics, 410 Haven Mews,
23 St Pauls Way, London, E3 4AG
Tel 020 8983 1323
Email victoriajardine@hotmail.co.uk
Website www.victoriajardine.com
Visitors welcome by appointment

166 John Jelfs Fellow
Cotswold Pottery, Clapton Row, Bourton-on-the-Water,
Cheltenham, Gloucestershire, GL54 2DN
Tel/Fax 01451 820173
Email pots@cotswoldpottery.co.uk
Website www.cotswoldpottery.co.uk
Showroom open Mon-Sat 9.30am-5pm,
Sun 10.30am-5pm

167 Jude Jelfs
Cotswold Pottery, Clapton Row, Bourton-on-the-Water,
Cheltenham, Gloucestershire, GL54 2DN
Tel/Fax 01451 820173
Email pots@cotswoldpottery.co.uk
Website www.cotswoldpottery.co.uk
Showroom open Mon-Sat 9.30am-5pm, Sun 10.30am-5pm

168 Chris Jenkins Fellow
19 Towngate, Marsden, Huddersfield, HD7 6DD
Tel 01484 844444

169 Linda John
Ty Llwyd, Dyffryn Ardudwy, Gwynedd, LL44 2EP
Tel 01341 247580
Email lindajohn@mac.com
Website www.lindajohn.co.uk

170 Wendy Johnson Fellow
8 Cromford Road, Wirksworth, Derbyshire, DE4 4FH
Tel 01629 822061
Email wendyjohnsonceramics@hotmail.com
Visitors welcome by appointment

171 Hazel Johnston Fellow
The Croft, North Street, Marton, Nr Rugby,
Warwickshire, CV23 9RJ
Tel 01926 632467
Visitors welcome by appointment

172 Emma Johnstone
The Blue Door Studio, c/o 34 Hawks Road,
Kingston upon Thames, Surrey, KT1 3EG
Tel 020 8549 7670 Mobile 07970 672535
Email embluedoor@aol.com
Visitors welcome by appointment

173 Philip Jolley
Tilly's House, St Edwards School, Oxford, OX2 7NN
Tel 01865 319257 Email jolleyp@stedwards.oxon.sch.uk

174 David Jones Fellow
21 Plymouth Place, Leamington Spa,
Warwickshire, CV31 1HN
Tel/Fax 01926 314643
Email davidjonesraku@lineone.net
Website www.davidjonesceramics.co.uk or
www.fixinglight-fixingfire.co.uk
Visitors welcome by appointment

175 Vresh David Kanikanian
Gallery Tavid, 56 St Mary's Road, Ealing, London, W5 5EX
Tel 020 8566 1494
Gallery hours: Weekdays 2-9pm; Sat-Sun 11am-9pm;
or by appointment

176 Lisa Katzenstein
67 Tyrwhitt Road London, SE4 1QE
Tel/Fax 020 8694 2428
Website www.lisakatzenstein.co.uk
Visitors welcome by appointment

177 Walter Keeler Fellow
Moorcroft Cottage, Penallt, Monmouth, Gwent, NP25 4AH
Tel 01600 713946 Fax 01600 712530
Visitors welcome by appointment

178 Chris Keenan Fellow
31 Balin House, Long Lane, London, SE1 1YQ
Tel 020 7701 2940 Fax 020 7403 1067
Email powellkeenan@compuserve.com
Website www.chriskeenan.com

179 Christy Keeney
Doon Glebe, Newmills, Letterkenny,
County Donegal, Ireland
Tel +353 (0)74 9167258
Email christykeeney@eircom.net

180 Dan Kelly
Home: 15 Bicknell Road, London, SE5 9AU
Workshop: Clockwork Studios, 38A Southwell Road,
London, SE5 9PG Tel 020 7733 1040

181 John Kershaw
40 Main Road, Windermere, Cumbria, LA23 1DY
Tel 01539 444844
Email john@kershawpottery.com
Website www.kershawpottery.com

182 Hyejeong Kim
Studio 8A, Iliffe Yard, Crampton Street,
London, SE17 3QA
Tel 07929 152128 Email hyejeong@nifty.com
Website www.potspots.co.uk

183 Ruth King Fellow
Rose Cottage, Main Street,
Shipton-by-Beningbrough, York, YO30 1AB
Tel 01904 470196
Email ruth@ruthkingceramics.com
Website www.ruthkingceramics.com
Visitors welcome by appointment

184 Gabriele Koch Fellow
Studio 147, 147 Archway Road,
Highgate, London, N6 5BL
Tel/Fax 020 8292 3169
Email gabrielekoch@blueyonder.co.uk
Visitors welcome by appointment

185 Daiva Kojelyte-Marrow
58 Queensgate, Northwich, Cheshire, CW8 1DU
Tel 01606 783619
Email james.marrow@manchester.ac.uk

186 Anna Lambert Fellow
Junction Workshop, 1 Skipton Road, Crosshills, North
Yorkshire, BD20 7SB
Tel 01535 631341 Email junction.works@virgin.net
Visitors welcome by appointment

187 Nigel Lambert Fellow
Golden Valley Cottage, Morse Lane, Drybrook,
Gloucestershire, GL17 9BA
Tel 01597 542251
Email nigel@nigellambertpotter.co.uk
Website www.nigellambertpotter.co.uk

188 Jean-Paul Landreau
Cross House, Tregaron, Ceredigion, SY25 6ND
Tel 01974 298828
Email ceramics@jeanpaullandreau.fsnet.co.uk
Website www.jean-paul-landreau.co.uk

189 Peter Lane Honorary Fellow
Ivy House, 44 Jacklyns Lane,
New Alresford, Hampshire, SO24 9LG
Tel 01962 735041 Email peter@studio-porcelain.co.uk
Website www.studio-porcelain.co.uk

190 Tony Laverick
Ridgeway House, Leek Road, Longsdon,
Staffordshire, ST9 9QF
Tel 01538 386050
Email tonylaverick@btinternet.com
Website www.churnetcontemporaryarts.co.uk
Visitors welcome by appointment

191 Liz Lawrence
40 The Nurseries, Langstone, Newport,
Monmouthshire, NP18 2NT
Tel 01633 411417 Mobile 07977 055563
Email liz_lawrence@lineone.net
Website www.southwalespotters.org.uk
Visitors welcome by appointment

192 Wendy Lawrence
Ty Tal, 34 Park Street, Denbigh,
Denbighshire, North Wales, LL16 3DB
Tel 01745 814441
Email wlawrenceceramics@hotmail.com
Website www.wendylawrenceceramics.com
Visitors welcome by appointment

193 John Leach Fellow
Muchelney Pottery, Nr Langport, Somerset, TA10 0DW
Tel 01458 250324 Fax 01458 253870
Website www.johnleachpottery.com

194 Roger Lewis
6 Chellow Terrace, Bradford, West Yorkshire, BD9 6AY
Tel 01274 495380
Email rogerlewis@theceramicartist.com
Website www.theceramicartist.com
Visitors welcome by appointment

195 Barbara Lock
UK: 44 Beatty Avenue, Cardiff, CF23 5QU
Tel 029 2075 5863 Email barbara@pottery.fsnet.co.uk
France: Le Bez, Vabre Tizac, 12240 France
Websites www.southwalespotters.org.uk
www.makersguildinwales.org.uk www.artmatters.org.uk

196 Anja Lubach
19 Wingrove Road, London, SE6 1QE
Tel 020 8695 9720 Email info@anjalubach.com
Website www.anjalubach.com
Wheel-thrown and altered vessels
Visitors welcome by appointment

197 Susan Luker
The Workshop, Hatch Court, Loddiswell,
Kingsbridge, Devon, TQ7 4AJ
Mobile 07779 923502
Email susanluker@raku.fsbusiness.co.uk
Visitors and school residencies by appointment

198 Martin Lungley
14 Tribune Drive, Houghton, Carlisle, Cumbria, CA3 0LE
Mobile 07811 038116 Email martinlungley@yahoo.com
Visitors welcome by appointment

199 Sophie MacCarthy
The Chocolate Factory, Farleigh Place,
Hackney, London, N16 7SX
Tel 020 7690 5091

200 Alasdair Neil MacDonell
2 Kennington Road, Bath, BA1 3EA
Tel 01225 465996
Email neil@macdonell-ceramics.co.uk
Website www.macdonell-ceramics.co.uk
Visitors welcome by appointment

201 Sally MacDonell
2 Kennington Road, Bath, BA1 3EA
Tel 01225 465996
Email sally@macdonell-ceramics.co.uk
Website www.macdonell-ceramics.co.uk
Visitors welcome by appointment

202 Ivar Stuart MacKay
Shire Pottery and Gallery Studios, Prudhoe Street,
Alnwick, Northumberland, NE66 1UW
Tel 01665 602277 Email ivar.porcelain@btconnect.com
Hand-thrown and turned reduction-fired studio porce-
lain. Crafts Council Photostore Selected Maker. Visits
by appointment only and during office hours, also
occasional exhibitions of fine art

203 Jane Maddison
The Old School Cottages,
Stragglethorpe, Lincoln, LN5 0QZ
Tel 01400 272971 Email jkmaddison@aol.com

204 Made in Cley
Made in Cley, High Street, Cley-next-the-Sea,
Nr Holt, Norfolk, NR25 7RF
Tel 01263 740134 Fax 01263 740186
Email madeincley@aol.com
Website www.madeincley.co.uk
The gallery is open all year, Mon-Sat 10am-5pm,
Sun 11am-4pm

205 Mal Magson Fellow
Jasmine Cottage, 3 Mount View, Muston,
Filey, North Yorkshire, YO14 0EL
Tel 01723 515568
Visitors welcome by appointment

206 Fenella Mallalieu Fellow
100 Mortimer Road, London, N1 4LA
Tel 020 7241 6553 Fax 020 7249 5341
Visitors welcome by appointment

207 Jim Malone Fellow
Dairy Lea Cottage, Lessonhall, Wigton, Cumbria, CA7 0EA
Tel 01697 345241
Visitors welcome

208 John Maltby Honorary Fellow
The Orchard House, Stoneshill, Crediton, Devon, EX17 4EF
Tel 01363 772753
Visitors welcome by appointment

209 West Marshall Fellow
118 White Hill, Chesham, Buckinghamshire, HP5 1AR
Tel 01494 785969 Email west.marshall@ntlworld.com
Website www.westmarshall.co.uk
Small showroom open to visitors by appointment

210 Will Levi Marshall Fellow
Holm Studio, Auchencairn, Castle Douglas, Dumfries
and Galloway, DG7 1QL
Tel 01556 640399 Fax 01556 640116
Mobile 07790 718783
Email will.marshall@btopenworld.com
Visitors welcome by appointment

211 Andrew Mason
3 Stiles Road, Alvaston, Derby, DE24 0PG
Tel 01332 753799
Email andymasonceramics@btinternet.com

212 Gareth Mason
7 Old Acre Road, Alton, Hampshire, GU34 1NR
Tel 01420 543573 Email gi.mason@virgin.net
Visitors welcome by appointment

213 May Ling Mason Fellow
3 Stiles Road, Alvaston, Derby, DE24 0PG
Tel 01332 753799
Email maylingceramics@btinternet.com

214 John Mathieson
50 Ridgeway, Weston Favell, Northampton, NN3 3AN
Tel 01604 409942 Email mathieson@ic24.net
Website www.studiopottery.co.uk or
www.theceramicartist.com
Visitors welcome by appointment

215 Marcio Mattos Fellow
7 Broadway Market Mews, Hackney, London, E8 4TS
Tel 020 7254 1351 Fax 020 7503 8417
Email marcio@musiclay.freeserve.co.uk
Website www.musiclay.freeserve.co.uk
Visitors welcome by appointment

216 Christine McCole
Hafod Hill Pottery, Llanboidy, Whitland,
Carmarthenshire, SA34 0ER
Tel 01994 448361 Email potters@hafodhillpottery.com
Website www.hafodhillpottery.com
Visitors welcome

217 Geraldine McGloin
147 Hatherley Gardens, London, E6 3HD
Tel/Fax 020 8552 8732
Email geraldine@geraldinemcgloin.com
Website www.geraldinemcgloin.com

218 Laurence McGowan Fellow
6 Aughton, Collingbourne Kingston,
Marlborough, Wiltshire, SN8 3SA
Tel 01264 850749
Email pottery@mcgowan.charitydays.co.uk
Website www.laurencemcgowan.co.uk
Visitors welcome by appointment

219 Hitomi McKenzie
10 Marian Road, Streatham Vale, London, SW16 5HR
Tel 020 8679 4181

220 Lesley McShea
Church Street Workshops, Guttridges Yard,
172 Stoke Newington Church Street, London, N16 0JL
Tel 020 7241 3676
Website www.geocities.com/lesleymcs

221 Martin McWilliam Fellow
Auf dem Kötjen 1, D-26209 Sandhatten, Germany
Tel +49 (0) 4482 8372
Email ceramics@martin-mcwilliam.de
Website www.martin-mcwilliam.de

222 Peter Meanley Fellow
6 Downshire Road, Bangor, County Down,
Northern Ireland, BT20 3TW
Tel/Fax 028 9146 6831
Email teapots@meanley.freeserve.co.uk
Visitors welcome by appointment

223 Eric James Mellon Honorary Fellow
5 Parkfield Avenue, Bognor Regis,
West Sussex, PO21 3BW
Tel 01243 268949
Visitors welcome by appointment

224 Kate Mellors
Mellors Garden Ceramics, Rosemead,
Marshwood, Bridport, Dorset, DT6 5QB
Tel/Fax 01297 678217
Email kate@mellors-ceramics.co.uk
Website www.mellors-ceramics.co.uk
Visitors welcome by appointment

225 Nick Membery
Waun Hir Pottery, Gwynfe Road,
Fflairfach, Llandeilo, SA19 6YT
Tel 01558 823099 Email nick.membery@btinternet.com
Website www.nickmembery.co.uk
Visitors welcome by appointment

226 David Miller Fellow
Rue du Ranc, 30190 Collorgues, France
Tel/Fax +33 (0) 466 819119
Email ceramicdavidmiller@yahoo.fr
Website www.ceramique.com/David-Miller

227 Sean Miller
108 Dewsbury Road, London, NW10 1EP
Tel 020 8208 0148   Mobile 07792 202477
Email seanpots@btinternet.com
Website www.theceramicartist.com

228 Toff Milway Fellow
Conderton Pottery, The Old Forge, Conderton, Nr
Tewkesbury, Gloucestershire, GL20 7PP
Tel/Fax 01386 725387   Website www.toffmilway.co.uk
Workshop and showroom open Mon-Sat 9am-5pm;
phone at other times. Always a large selection of work
on display

229 Ursula Mommens Honorary Fellow
The Pottery, South Heighton,
Newhaven, Sussex, BN9 0HL
Tel 01273 514408

230 Sarah Monk
Eastnor Pottery, Home Farm, Eastnor,
Ledbury, Herefordshire, HR8 1RD
Tel/Fax 01531 633886
Email eastnor.pottery@ukonline.co.uk
Website www.eastnorpottery.co.uk
Visitors welcome by appointment

231 Aki Moriuchi Fellow
Home: 4 Menhyr Drive, Carbis Bay,
St Ives, Cornwall TR26 2QR
Tel 01736 793064
Studio: Gaolyard Studios, Dove Street,
St Ives, Cornwall TR26 2LZ
Email akimoriuchi@hotmail.com
Website www.gaolyard-studio-pottery.co.uk
Visitors to the studio welcome by appointment

232 Ursula Morley Price
Chez Gaty, Vaux-Lavalette, 16320 France
Tel/Fax +33 (0) 545 259167

233 Catrin Mostyn Jones
Drumcroon Gallery, 2 Parsons Walk, Wigan, WN1 1RS
Mobile 07787 507228
Email vividceramics@hotmail.com
Website www.vividceramics.co.uk

234 Roger Mulley
Clanfield Pottery, 131 Chalton Lane, Clanfield,
Waterlooville, Hampshire, PO8 0RQ
Tel 023 9259 5144   Fax 023 9235 1499
Email info@rogermulleyceramics.co.uk
Website www.rogermulleyceramics.co.uk

235 John Mullin
September House, Parnacott, Holsworthy,
Devon, EX22 7JD
Tel/Fax 01409 253589
Email mullinceramics@msn.com
Website www.mullin.uk.tt
Visitors welcome by appointment

236 Stephen Murfitt
The Workshop, 18 Stretham Road, Wicken,
Cambridgeshire, CB7 5XH   Tel 01353 721160
Visitors welcome by appointment

237 Claire Murray
The Old Coach House, Ashreigney,
Chulmleigh, Devon, EX18 7NB
Tel 01769 520775
Email clairemurray@btinternet.com
Visitors welcome by appointment

238 Emily Myers Fellow
2 Chalkpit Cottages, Tangley, Andover,
Hampshire, SP11 0RX
Tel 01264 730243   Email emily@emilymyers.com
Website www.emilymyers.com
Visitors welcome by appointment

239 Susan Nemeth Fellow
Unit G6, The Chocolate Factory, Farleigh Place,
Stoke Newington, London, N16 7SX
Mobile 07855 002678   Email susan@snemeth.fsnet.co.uk
Website www.hiddenart.com/susannemeth
Please email or phone for open studio
details or an appointment

240 Christine Niblett
Carrer Xesc Forteza 5, Valldemossa,
07170 Mallorca, Spain
Tel +34 (0) 971 616172 or 020 7824 8625
Fax +34 (0) 971 616098
Visitors welcome by appointment

241 Jeremy Nichols
32A Sellons Avenue, London, NW10 4HH
Tel 020 8961 0409
Email jeremy@nichols70.freeserve.co.uk
Visitors to my Broxbourne, Hertfordshire, studio are
welcome. Please contact me for directions.

242 Jacqueline Norris
81 High Street Eton, Windsor, Berkshire, SL4 6AF
Tel 01753 622333
Email jacqueline@etonappliedarts.co.uk
Visitors welcome to the gallery at any time, studio vis-
its by appointment only. Open Tues-Sat 10am-6pm

243 Marcus O'Mahony
Glencairn Pottery, Lismore, County Waterford, Ireland
Tel +353 (0) 58 56694   Email info@marcusomahony.com
Website www.marcusomahony.com
Visitors welcome to the workshop and small
gallery by appointment

244 Jitka Palmer
3 Florence Park, Westbury Park, Bristol, BS6 7LS
Tel 0117 924 3473
Email jitka.palmer@bigfoot.com
Website www.jitkapalmer.co.uk
Visitors welcome by appointment

245 Sue Paraskeva
Studio One, Jubilee Stores, The Quay, Newport,
Isle of Wight, PO30 2EF
Tel 01983 522399   Email sue@paraskevapots.com
Website www.sueparaskeva.co.uk
Visitors welcome by appointment

246 Stephen Parry
Ryburgh Pottery, Little Ryburgh,
Fakenham, Norfolk, NR21 OLP
Tel 01328 829543
Email steve@ryburghpottery.fsnet.co.uk
Showroom at the pottery

247 Colin Pearson Honorary Fellow
Mews House, 98-100 Tottenham Road, London, N1 4DP
Tel/Fax 020 7923 2577   Mobile 07958 387744
No longer actively potting

248 Jane Perryman Fellow
Wash Cottage, Clare Road, Hundon, Suffolk, CO10 8DH
Tel 01440 786228   Email janeperryman@btinternet.com
Website www.janeperryman.com
Visitors welcome by appointment

249 Richard Phethean Fellow
2 Hillfield, Sibford Ferris, Banbury, Oxfordshire, OX15 5QS
Tel 01295 780041
Email phethean@clara.co.uk
Website www.phethean.clara.net
Visitors welcome by appointment

250 Ian Pirie Fellow
8 St Michael's Place, Newton Hill, Stonehaven,
Aberdeenshire, AB39 3SG
Tel 01569 730908 or 01224 263608

251 John Pollex Fellow
Stowford House, 43 Seymour Avenue, St Judes,
Plymouth, Devon, PL4 8RB
Tel 01752 224902
Email john@johnpollex.co.uk
Website www.johnpollex.co.uk

252 Philomena Pretsell
Rose Cottage, 10 Fountain Place, Loanhead,
Midlothian, Scotland, EH20 9EA
Tel/Fax 0131 440 0751
Workshop at home, five miles from centre of
Edinburgh; visitors welcome by appointment

253 Marie Prett
Home: 1 Eason Villas, Maidstone Road, Marden,
Tonbridge, Kent, TN12 9AD
Studio: The Pottery Workshop, Mote Cottage,
Howlands Road, Marden, Kent, TN12 9LB
Tel 01622 832150   Mobile 07759 778868
Website www.marieprett.co.uk
Visitors welcome by appointment

254 Paul Priest
71 Sunnycroft, Downley, High Wycombe,
Buckinghamshire, HP13 5UR
Tel 01494 639819   Fax 01494 639951
Email paulwpriest@aol.com

255 Jacqui Ramrayka
Archway Ceramics, 410 Haven Mews,
23 St Paul's Way, London E3 4AG
Tel 020 8983 1323 Mobile 07973 771687
Email info@jacquiramrayka.com
Website www.jacquiramrayka.com

256 Jacqueline Rankin
Jacqueline Rankin Sculptural Ceramics, 45 West View
Road, Sutton Coldfield, West Midlands, B75 6AZ
Tel 0121 378 1844 Email jrsceramics@btinternet.com

257 Nick Rees Fellow
Muchelney Pottery, Muchelney, Nr Langport,
Somerset, TA10 0DW
Tel 01458 250324

258 Petra Reynolds
Wobage Farm, Upton Bishop, Ross-on-Wye,
Herefordshire, HR9 7QP
Tel 01989 780448 Fax 01989 780495
Wobage Makers Gallery open Apr-Sept: Thurs-Sun
10am-5pm; Oct-Mar: Sat-Sun only; other times by
appointment only

259 Mary Rich Fellow
Penwerris Pottery, Cowlands Creek, Old Kea,
Nr Truro, Cornwall, TR3 6AT
Tel 01872 276926
Visitors are welcome to visit the workshop; please
telephone first for directions

260 Christine-Ann Richards Fellow
Chapel House, High Street, Wanstrow,
Nr Shepton Mallet, Somerset, BA4 4TE
Tel/Fax 01749 850208
Email mail@christineannrichards.co.uk
Website www.christineannrichards.co.uk
Visitors welcome by appointment

261 Audrey Richardson
Morawel, Parrog Road, Newport, Pembrokeshire, SA42 0RF
Tel 01239 820449
Visitors welcome by appointment

262 David Roberts Fellow
UK: Cressfield House, 44 Upperthong Lane, Holmfirth,
Huddersfield, Yorkshire, HD9 3BQ
Tel 01484 685110
Italy: 14 Via Castello, Castello de Comano, 54015
Comano, MS, Italy
Mobile +44 (0) 7985 021111
Email david@davidroberts-ceramics.com
Website www.davidroberts-ceramics.com

263 Hilary Roberts
11 Carlton Street, Halifax, HX1 2AL
Tel 01422 320879 Email hilaryceramics@hotmail.com

264 Jim Robison Fellow
Booth House Gallery, 3 Booth House,
Holmfirth, Huddersfield, HD9 2QT
Tel/Fax 01484 685270 Email jim.robison@virgin.net
Website www.jimrobison.co.uk or
www.boothhousegallery.co.uk

265 Emma Rodgers Fellow
12 Birch Road, Oxton, Wirral, Cheshire, CH43 5UA
Tel/Fax 0151 652 3040
Website www.emmarodgers.co.uk
Studio not open to public

266 Phil Rogers Fellow
Marston Pottery, Lower Cefn Faes,
Rhayader, Powys, LD6 5LT
Tel 01597 810875
Email phil@marstonpottery.wanadoo.co.uk
Website www.philrogerspottery.com
Opening hours Mon-Sun 9.30am-5.30pm;
please telephone if coming a long distance

267 Margaret Rollason
19 Oakside Close, Evington, Leicestershire, LE5 6SN
Tel 0116 241 2188

268 Duncan Ross Fellow
Daneshay House, 69A Alma Lane, Upper Hale,
Farnham, Surrey, GU9 0LT
Tel 01252 710704
Email duncan@duncanrossceramics.co.uk
Website www.duncanrossceramics.co.uk
Visitors to studio showroom welcome by appointment

269 Elisabeth Roussel
26 High Street, Woodstock, Oxfordshire, OX20 1TG
Tel 01993 811298 Email leroussel@aol.com
Visitors welcome by appointment

270 Antonia Salmon Fellow
20 Adelaide Road, Nether Edge, Sheffield, S7 1SQ
Tel 0114 258 5971 Email antoniasalmon@hemscott.net
Website www.antoniasalmon-ceramics.co.uk
Visitors welcome by appointment

271 Robert Sanderson Fellow
PO Box 612, Scariff, County Clare, Republic of Ireland
Tel/Fax +353 (0) 61 922918
Email thelogbook@eircom.net
Website www.thelogbook.net

272 Colin Saunders
3 Chapel Cottages, Withersdale Street,
Nr Harleston, Norfolk, IP20 0JG
Tel 01379 588278
Not open to the public

273 Micki Schloessingk Fellow
Bridge Pottery, Cheriton,
Nr Llanmadoc, Gower, Swansea, SA3 1BY
Tel 01792 386499
Email micki@mickisaltglaze.co.uk
Website www.mickisaltglaze.co.uk
Visitors welcome most Fri-Sat 10am-5pm and often at
other times; please phone to check (closed January)

274 David Scott Fellow
22B Manor Road, Loughborough, Leicestershire, LE11 2LY
Tel 01509 228955 Email d.scott1@lboro.ac.uk

275 Sarah Jane Selwood Fellow
13 Hamilton Terrace, Edinburgh, EH15 1NB
Tel 0131 620 1291 Email sj@sjs-ceramics.info
Visitors welcome by appointment

276 Claire Seneviratne
15 Romeo Arbour, Heathcote,
Warwick Gates, Warwick, CV34 6FD
Tel 01926 426006
Email claire@seneviratne.co.uk
Website www.claire.seneviratne.co.uk
Visitors welcome by appointment

277 Kathy Shadwell
24 Priory Avenue, North Cheam, Surrey, SM3 8LX
Tel 020 8644 7471 Email jrwhiting@tiscali.co.uk
Visitors welcome by appointment

278 Jeremy Sharp
1 Lychpole Farm Cottages, Titch Hill,
Sompting, West Sussex, BN15 0AY
Tel 01903 763021
Email jay@lychpolefarm.fsnet.co.uk
Visitors welcome by appointment

279 Simon Sharp
Port-Hole Gallery, Pont-Ar-Sais, Carmarthen, SA32 7DN
Tel 01267 253814
Visitors welcome by appointment

280 Andy Shaw
15 Manor Mews, Mickleover Manor,
Mickleover, Derby, DE3 0SH
Tel/Fax 01332 523737 Email andyshaw.art@virgin.net

281 Georgia Shearman
27 Stevens Crescent, Tatterdown, Bristol, BS3 4UH
Tel 0117 971 0071

282 Shelton Pottery
18 Heath End Road, Alsager, Cheshire, ST7 2SQ
Tel/Fax 01270 872686 Email sheltonpottery@aol.com

283 Alan Sidney Fellow
Minhafren Mill, Aberbechan, Newtown, Powys, SY16 3AW
Tel 01686 630644

284 Ray Silverman Fellow
29 Wordsworth Gardens, Borehamwood,
Hertfordshire, WD6 2AB
Tel/Fax 020 8905 2441 Mobile 07747 636772
Email raymondsilverman@hotmail.com
Visitors welcome by appointment

285 Anna Silverton
41 Burghill Road, Sydenham, London, SE26 4HJ
Tel 020 8659 0767 Email annasilverton@hotmail.com
Visitors welcome by appointment

286 Penny Simpson
The Studio, 44A Court Street,
Moretonhampstead, Devon, TQ13 8LG
Tel/Fax 01647 440708
Email psimpson@thestudiopots.fsnet.co.uk
Workshop and showroom open to visitors, Mon-Fri
9.30am-5pm and some weekends; telephone first if
making special journey

287 Daniel Smith
Archway Ceramics, 410 Haven Mews,
23 St Paul's Way, London, E3 4AG
Tel 020 8983 1323
Email danielsmith@w3e3.freeserve.co.uk

288 Elizabeth Smith
Millhead House, Millhead, Bampton,
Nr Tiverton, Devon, EX16 9LP
Tel/Fax 01398 331442 Email smithmillhead@aol.com
Visitors are welcome at my display studio and
workshop by appointment

289 Mark Smith
11 School Lane, Sudbury, Ashbourne,
Derbyshire, DE6 5HZ
Tel 01283 585219
Visitors welcome by appointment

290 Peter Smith Fellow
Higher Bojewyan, Pendeen, Penzance,
Cornwall, TR19 7TR
Tel 01736 788820 Email petersmith1@lineone.net
Visitors welcome by appointment

291 Rob Sollis
UK: Fishacre Pottery, Littlehempston,
Totnes, Devon, TQ9 6NF
Mobile 07748 288958
Portugal: Ceramica de Rob Sollis, Barregao, APTO 141,
7320999 Castelo de Vide, Alentejo, Portugal
Tel +351 (0) 245 905359
Email fishacre@rob-sollis.co.uk
Website www.rob-sollis.co.uk

292 Chris Speyer Fellow
Yerja Ceramics and Textiles, Mill Rise, Ford Road,
Bampton, Devon, EX16 9LW
Tel/Fax 01398 331163
Email chris.speyer@btinternet.com

293 Alison Stace
Home: 4 Streatham Court,
Streatham High Road, London, SW16 1DL
Studio: Whirled Art Studios, 259-260 Hardess Street,
Loughborough Junction, London SE24 0HN
Mobile 07930 105267 Email astace@acblack.com
Visitors welcome by appointment

294 Jeremy Steward Fellow
Wobage Farm, Upton Bishop, Ross-on-Wye,
Herefordshire, HR9 7QP
Tel 01989 780448 Fax 01989 780495
Wobage Makers Gallery open Apr-Sept: Thurs-Sun
10am-5pm; Oct-Mar: Sat-Sun only; other times by
appointment only

295 Helen Swain Fellow
8 Fyfield Road, Walthamstow, London, E17 3RG
Tel 020 8520 4043
Visitors welcome by appointment

296 Geoffrey Swindell Fellow
18 Laburnum Way, Dinas Powys,
Vale of Glamorgan, CF64 4TH
Email geoff@dell18.freeserve.co.uk
Website www.geoffreyswindellceramics.co.uk
Visitors welcome by appointment

297 Taja
Pottery House, 38 Cross Street,
Moretonhampstead, Devon, TQ13 8NL
Tel 01647 440782 Email hitaja@hotmail.com

298 Nicola Tassie
Standpoint Studios, 45 Coronet Street, London, N1 6HD
Tel 020 7729 5292 Fax 020 7739 4921
Visitors welcome by appointment

299 Kaori Tatebayashi
401½ Workshops, 401½ Wandsworth Road,
London, SW8 2JP
Mobile 07816 422033 Email info@kaoriceramics.com
Website www.kaoriceramics.com
Opening hours Mon-Fri 10am-6pm; visitors by
appointment only

300 Rebecca Taylor
Home: 18 Clarion House, St Anne's Court,
Soho, London, W1F 0BA
Tel 020 7434 2924
Studio: Goodlands Cottage, Botany Bay Lane,
Chislehurst, Kent, BR7 5PT
Mobile 07960 942007

301 Yo Thom
A115 Faircharm Studios, 8-12 Creekside,
Deptford, London, SE8 3DX
Tel 020 8305 8427 Email yodekune@hotmail.com
Visitors welcome by appointment; opening hours
10am-5pm

302 Fiona Thompson
Dumfries and Galloway Arts Association Ltd, Gracefield
Art Centre, 28 Edinburgh Road, Dumfries, DG1 1JQ
Mobile 07901 930654 Email fi_ceramics@hotmail.com
Visitors welcome by appointment

303 Owen Thorpe Fellow
Priestweston Pottery, The Chapel, Priestweston,
Chirbury, Montgomery, Powys, SY15 6DE
Tel 01938 561618
Visitors welcome by appointment

304 Deborah Timperley
59 Smithbarn, Horsham, West Sussex, RH13 6DT
Tel 01403 265835
Email deborah.timperley@btinternet.com
Website www.studiopottery.co.uk or
www.portfoliocity.com/deborahtimperley
Visitors welcome by appointment

305 Marianne de Trey Honorary Fellow
The Cabin, Shinners Bridge, Totnes, Devon, TQ9 6JB
Tel 01803 862046 (after 6.00pm)
Visitors by appointment

306 Fran Tristram
Lady Bay Pottery, 42 Seymour Road,
West Bridgford, Nottingham, NG2 5EF
Tel 0115 982 2681
Email frantristram@ntlworld.com
Website www.nottinghamstudios.org.uk/ladybay
Visitors welcome by appointment

307 Ruthanne Tudball Fellow
Temple Barn Pottery, Solomon's Temple, Welborne,
Dereham, Norfolk, NR20 3LD
Tel 01362 858770
Email ruthanne@ruthannetudball.com or
ruthanne_tudball@btopenworld.com
Website www.ruthannetudball.com
Visitors are welcome to my studio and showroom all
year round, but advisable to telephone first

308 Craig Underhill
8 Prescot Road, Stourbridge, West Midlands, DY9 7LD
Tel 01384 376559
Email craigunderhill@waitrose.com
Visitors welcome by appointment

309 Sue Varley
54 Elthorne Road, Uxbridge, Middlesex, UB8 2PS
Tel 01895 231738
Email suevarley@btconnect.com
Visitors welcome by appointment

310 Tina Vlassopulos Fellow
29 Canfield Gardens, London, NW6 3JP
Tel 020 7624 4582 Fax 020 7328 1483
Email tina@4tuna.fsnet.co.uk
Visitors welcome by appointment

311 Jonathan Wade
Tarmount Studios, 2 Tarmount Lane,
Shoreham-by-Sea, West Sussex, BN43 6DA
Mobile 07733 268005
Visitors welcome by appointment

312 Carol Wainwright
Currantberry Hall Farm, Hull Road,
Wilberfoss, York, YO41 5PD
Tel 01759 380544
Visitors welcome by appointment

313 Motoko Watana
Gaolyard Studios, Dove Street, St Ives,
Cornwall, TR26 2LZ
Tel 01736 799336 Email wakanamoto@hotmail.com
Website www.gaolyard-studio-pottery.co.uk

314 Clare Wakefield
10 Station Road, Walmer, Deal, Kent, CT14 7QR
Tel 01304 239771 Email clarewakefield@aol.com
Website www.clarewakefield.co.uk
Visitors welcome by appointment

315 Josie Walter Fellow
22 Nan Gells Hill, Bolehill, Derbyshire, DE4 4GN
Tel/Fax 01629 823669 Email josie@josiewalter.co.uk
Website www.josiewalter.co.uk
Visitors welcome by appointment

316 Sarah Walton Fellow
Keeper's, Bo-Peep Lane, Alciston,
Nr Polegate, East Sussex, BN26 6UH
Tel/Fax 01323 811517
Email sarah.walton@freenet.co.uk
Website www.sarahwalton.co.uk
The pottery is open 11am-5pm weekdays, weekends by
appointment; advisable to telephone in advance

317 John Ward Fellow
Fachongle Uchaf, Cilgwyn, Newport,
Pembrokeshire, SA42 0QR
Tel 01239 820706
Email john@ward-wales.freeserve.co.uk
Visitors welcome by appointment

318 Sasha Wardell Fellow
36 Tory, Bradford on Avon, Wiltshire, BA15 1NN
Tel 01225 868756 Mobile 07855 110603
Email swardell@dircon.co.uk
Website www.studiopottery.co.uk
Visitors welcome by appointment

319 Annette Welch
21 Colyton Road, East Dulwich, London, SE22 0NE
Tel 020 8693 9400 Email annettewelch@mac.com

320 Nicola Werner
Nicola Werner Pottery, Burcombe Farm, Bolham Water,
Clayhidon, Nr Cullompton, Devon, EX15 3QB
Tel 01823 680957 Website www.nicolawerner.com

321 Gilda Westermann Fellow
2 The Shrubbery, Topsham, Exeter, EX3 0DW
Tel 01392 873622 Email g.westermann@freeuk.com
Website www.g.westermann.freeuk.com
Visitors welcome by appointment

322 John Wheeldon Fellow
4 West End, Wirksworth, Derbyshire, DE4 4EG
Tel 01629 822356 Email j.wheeldon@tiscali.co.uk
Website www.johnwheeldonceramics.co.uk

323 Rob Whelpton
20 Bishopstrow, Warminster, Wiltshire, BA12 9HN
Tel 01985 219577 Email info@krukker.com
Website www.krukker.com
Visitors welcome by appointment

324 Whichford Pottery
Whichford Pottery, Whichford, Nr Shipston-on-Stour,
Warwickshire, CV36 5PG
Tel 01608 684416
Email sgraffito@whichfordpottery.com
Opening hours Mon-Fri 9am-5pm, Sat & Bank Holidays
10am-4pm, Sun (Apr-Sept only) 11am-4pm

325 David White Fellow
4 Callis Court Road, Broadstairs, Kent, CT10 3AE
Tel 01843 863145 Email didave@white-art.co.uk
Website www.theceramicartist.com
Visitors welcome by appointment

326 Mary White Fellow
Zimmerplatzweg 6, 55599 Wonsheim, Germany
Tel +49 (0) 6703 2922 Fax +49 (0) 6703 305833
Email mary.white@t-online.de

327 Tony White
Upper Lodge, Hafod, Cymystwyth,
Ystrad Meurig, Ceredigion, SY25 6DX
Tel 01974 282202 Email tonyjohnwhite@btinternet.com
Website www.tonywhiteceramics.co.uk

328 Caroline Whyman Fellow
21 Iliffe Yard, Crampton Street, London, SE17 3QA
Mobile 07958 908450 Fax 020 7820 8207
Email whyman@dircon.co.uk
Visitors by appointment

329 Jon Williams
Eastnor Pottery, Home Farm, Eastnor, Ledbury,
Herefordshire, HR8 1RD Tel/Fax 01531 633886
Email eastnor.pottery@ukonline.co.uk
Website www.eastnorpottery.co.uk or
www.flyingpotter.com
Visitors welcome by appointment

330 Maggie Williams

Poulders, 65 Ospringe Street,
Ospringe, Faversham, Kent, ME13 8TW
Tel 01795 531768
Email mw2@canterbury.ac.uk
Visitors welcome by appointment

331 Peter Wills

Home: 44 Newcastle Hill, Bridgend,
South Wales, CF31 4EY
Tel 01656 662902 Mobile 07790 100183
Studio/Gallery: 8 Park Street, Bridgend, CF31 4AU
Email peter@peterwills.co.uk
Website www.peterwills.co.uk
Visitors to studio welcome by appointment: Mon-Fri
10am-5.30pm, Sat 10am-2pm; other times by
arrangement

332 Richard Wilson

Chapel Yard Pottery, Abbotsbury,
Weymouth, Dorset, DT3 4JR
Email lwilson@toucansurf.com
Website www.chapelyard.co.uk
Workshop open to the public: Tues-Sat 9am-5pm

333 David Winckley Fellow

Vellow Pottery, Lower Vellow,
Williton, Taunton, Somerset, TA4 4LS
Tel 01984 656458
Workshop and pottery shop open Mon-Sat 8.30am-6pm

334 Tessa Wolfe Murray

Biscuit Studio, 12B Wilbury Grove,
Hove, East Sussex, BN3 3JQ
Tel 01273 720625
Email tessa@wolfemurrayceramics.co.uk
Website www.wolfemurrayceramics.co.uk
Visitors welcome by appointment

335 Mary Wondrausch Honorary Fellow

The Pottery, Brickfields, Compton,
Nr Guildford, Surrey, GU3 1HZ
Tel 01483 414097
Opening hours: Mon-Fri 10am-1pm, 2-4pm;
Sat-Sun 2-4pm; please telephone first

336 Gary Wood Fellow

One Two Five, Box Road, Bath, BA1 7LR
Tel/Fax 01225 858888
Email garywood@theceramicartist.com

337 Philip Wood

Linden Mead Studio, Whatley,
Nr Frome, Somerset, BA11 3JX
Tel 01373 836425 Email philipwood1@gmail.com
Visitors welcome by appointment

338 Rachel Wood

11 Murray Street, Mansfield, Nottinghamshire, NG18 4AR
Tel 01623 642425 Email rachel.wood1@tiscali.co.uk

339 Steve Woodhead Fellow

65 Shakespeare Gardens, Rugby,
Warwickshire, CV22 6HA
Tel 01788 522178
Website and email via www.teapotbook.com
Visitors welcome by appointment

340 Rosemary Wren Honorary Fellow

The Oxshott Pottery, Nutwood Steading,
Strathpeffer, Ross and Cromartie, IV14 9DT
Tel 01997 421478
Although The Oxshott Pottery is no longer in production there are still many pieces of historical interest for
sale. There are no fixed opening hours, but potential
purchasers are requested to make contact by telephone

341 Gill Wright

52 South Street, Epsom, Surrey, KT18 7PQ
Tel 01372 723908
Workshop in Headley. Visitors welcome by appointment

342 Takeshi Yasuda Fellow

Garden Flat, 14 Grosvenor Place, Bath BA1 6AX
Tel 01225 334136 (Home) or 01225 313492 (Studio)
Mobile 07815 068146 Email t.yasuda@btinternet.com

343 Alistair Young

Guy Hall Cottage, Awre, Newnham-on-Severn,
Gloucestershire, GL14 1EL
Tel 01594 510343 Email email@alistairyoung.co.uk
Website www.alistairyoung.co.uk
Visitors welcome by appointment

344 Paul Young

Station Pottery, Shenton Station, Shenton, Nr
Nuneaton, Warwickshire, CV13 0AA
Mobile 07711 628337
Email potterpaulyoung@hotmail.com
Workshop open most weekends, advisable to
telephone first

Location Map

Location Map

The following pages give approximate locations for all members in the UK and Ireland. Locations correspond to numbers on the address pages in this section. It is advisable to telephone before making a special journey, or where potters state visits by appointment only.

Members not based in the UK:
Spain – 11, 240
France – 87, 226, 232
Germany – 221, 326

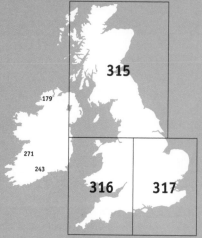

315

179

271

243

316   **317**

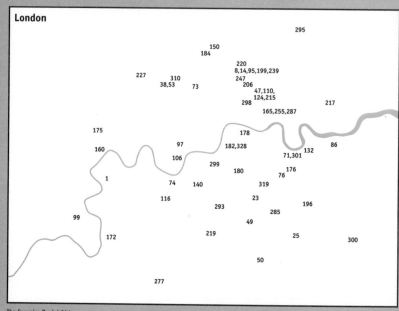

London

295

150
184

220
8,14,95,199,239
247
206
47,110,
124,215
298
217
165,255,287

227
38,53
310
73

178

182,328

97
106

299
180
319
76
71,301
132
86
176

175

160

1

74
140

116

23
293
285
196

99

49

219
25
300

172

50

277

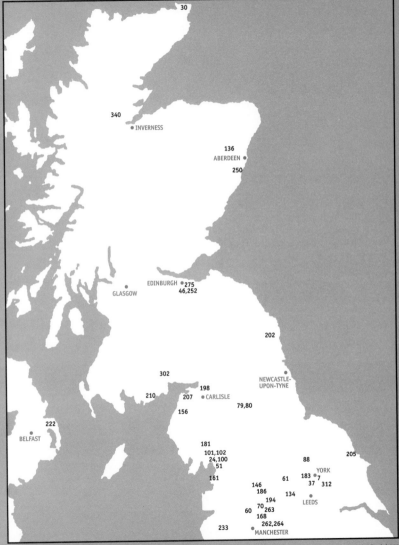

30

340
● INVERNESS

136
ABERDEEN ●
250

EDINBURGH ● 275
46,252
GLASGOW ●

202

302
NEWCASTLE-
UPON-TYNE ●
198
210   207   ● CARLISLE
156   79,80

222
BELFAST ●
181
101,102
24,100
51   88   205
161   146   61   183 ● YORK
                 186   37 312
          60 70 194 134   ● LEEDS
              168 263
          262,264
233   ● MANCHESTER

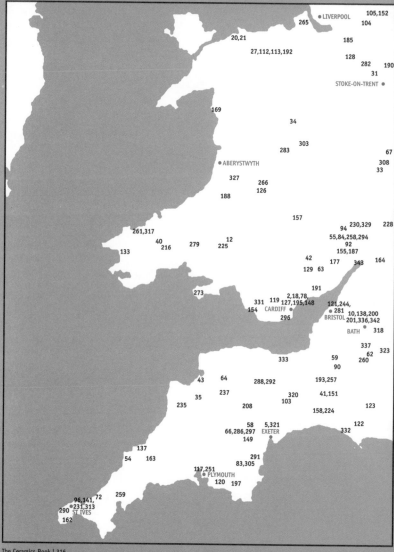

LIVERPOOL

265

105,152
104

185

128

282 190

31

20,21

27,112,113,192

STOKE-ON-TRENT

169

34

303

283

67

308

33

ABERYSTWYTH

327

266
126

188

157

94 230,329 228

55,84,258,294

92

155,187

261,317

40

133 216

279

12
225

42

129 63

177 343 164

191

273

331 119 2,18,78,

154 127,195,148

CARDIFF

296

121,244,

281

BRISTOL 10,138,200

201,336,342

BATH 318

337

62 323

59 260

90

333

43 64

288,292

193,257

41,151

35 237

320

208 103

123

235

158,224

122

332

58 5,321

66,286,297 EXETER

149

291

83,305

137

54 163

117,251

PLYMOUTH

120 197

96,141, 72

231,313 259

290 ST IVES

162

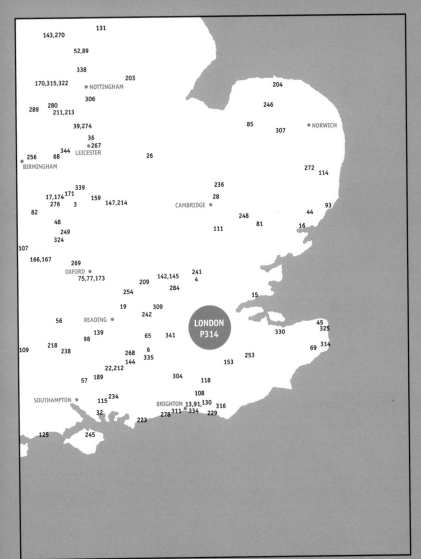

131
143,270
52,89
338
170,315,322   203
● NOTTINGHAM   204
306   246
289 280
211,213   85
39,274   307   ● NORWICH
36
● 267
256 68 344   26
LEICESTER   272
BIRMINGHAM   114
339   236
17,174 171   28
276   3   159   147,214   44   93
82   CAMBRIDGE ●
48   248   16
249   81
324   111
107
166,167
269 ●
OXFORD ●
75,77,173   142,145   241
209   4
254   284   15
19   309
242   330   45
56   325
READING ●
98 139   65   341   69   314
109   253
218   6
238   268   335
144   153
22,212
57 189   304   118
108
SOUTHAMPTON ●   115 234   BRIGHTON 13,91,130
32   278 311 334   316
223   229
125   245

LONDON
P314

About the Craft Potters Association

The Craft Potters Association of Great Britain (CPA) was established in 1958, and is the national body representing ceramic artists in the UK. Its aim is to advance and encourage the creation of fine works in ceramics, and to foster and extend the interests of the public in such objects and to promote their value in society. The CPA was founded by a small group of potters as a Friendly Society and now has some 150 Fellows, 200 Professional and 500 Associate Members including internationally recognised makers as well as many potters at the start of their careers. If you are interested in joining the CPA either as an Associate Member or as a Professional Member (membership by selection) please contact cpa@ceramicreview.com for details.

Contemporary Ceramics

The CPA owns and operates Contemporary Ceramics, the leading studio ceramics gallery in London's West End, where an ever-changing spectrum of members work is always on display and available for sale. We also stock an extensive range of ceramic books which you can browse in the gallery or online at www.cpaceramics.com where they can be purchased.

Ceramic Review

The CPA also publishes *Ceramic Review*, the International Magazine of Ceramic Art and Craft. *Ceramic Review* is published bimonthly and is recognised as one of the world's leading journals on contemporary ceramics. To purchase your subscription online visit www.ceramicreview.com

Educational Activities

Promotion of interest in studio ceramics is a key element of the work of the CPA and to this end it arranges a full programme of educational events for members and the general public, including talks by leading potters, demonstrations and visits to studios, and in co-operation with regional and national potter's societies arranges events and talks in different parts of the country and internationally.

In the 1990s the CPA, in partnership with Rufford Ceramic Centre, Nottinghamshire, initiated the Ceramic Fairs, aimed at introducing the general public to studio ceramics. Along similar lines, the CPA now organises *Oxford Studio Ceramics*, at St Edward's School, Oxford, showing the work of some sixty selected makers (www.oxfordsc.co.uk). In 2005 the CPA launched *Ceramic Art London*, a major international fair and educational programme, held at the Royal College of Art, London (www.ceramics.org.uk). These highly successful events are a valuable and important part of the CPA's interaction with the public in seeking to promote the work of individual artists and to find new audiences.

Charitable Trust

In 1991 the CPA set up the Craft Pottery Charitable Trust to support educational activities. Trustees include a member of the Crafts Council and former officials and current members of the CPA. Funding for the Charitable Trust comes from donations from the CPA operating companies and from personal donations, bequests and other fundraising activities organised and supported by members.

The Trust has several grant schemes including an annual award of grants up to £1,000 in value, as well as occasional awards such as the Mick Casson Memorial Award for functional ware. Applications for the annual grant scheme must be submitted by 15th December and decisions are announced the following February.

Each year, at Contemporary Ceramics, the CPA organises the *Setting Out* exhibition, which is designed to launch new graduates on their ceramics careers. Colleges are invited to submit the work of two students for selection for the exhibition. The entrants may also apply to the Charitable Trust for a bursary of £500 to enable them to carry out individual postgraduate projects.

Email cpa@ceramicreview.com for further details about the work of the Charitable Trust.

Top: *Ceramic Art London*; Bottom left: *Ceramic Review*; Bottom right: Contemporary Ceramics